MORE QUIZZLES

by
Wayne Williams

A resource for developing logic skills

Published by arrangement with
THE BERKLEY PUBLISHING GROUP, NEW YORK.

Educational Edition

Produced by

DALE
SEYMOUR
PUBLICATIONS
P.O. BOX 10888
PALO ALTO, CA 94303

Educational Edition designed by Dale Seymour Publications
Exclusive license to publish granted to Dale Seymour Publications
arranged by The Berkley Publishing Group, New York.

Copyright © 1982 by Grosset & Dunlap, Inc.
Printed in the United States of America
Dale Seymour Publications Printing: January, 1984

ISBN 0-86651-208-X

Order Number DS01469

abcdefghi-MA-8987654

PROBLEM SOLVING WITH MORE QUIZZLES

The National Council of Teachers of Mathematics, an organization of professional educators, recommends that the number one priority for the 1980s for mathematics teachers is to make problem solving the focus of their instruction.

Problem solving includes a broad range of strategies. One of the important strategies for solving problems is deductive logic. This strategy is often the only one needed to solve a problem. This book presents a number of problems using this particular strategy.

How to Use This Book

The problems in this first edition of MORE QUIZZLES, just as in the original QUIZZLES, are especially designed as student worksheets. They were made to be duplicated. Limited reproduction permission is granted to provide a classroom set of materials. This book solves a sample quizzle step-by-step so you can give your students ideas about how to use the clue charts.

The type and charts are large—sufficiently large for overhead transparency use with class-developed lessons. Also, the quizzle solutions can be put on a chart and presented on the overhead.

It is not likely that any class will solve all 48 quizzles. As the puzzle numbers increase, the puzzles become more difficult. You may decide to use the later puzzles as enrichment exercises for your gifted students or students who particularly enjoy logic problems.

WELCOME TO QUIZZLES

Because Quizzles are logic problems, and because people think differently, there are many routes to the one correct answer to each quizzle.

We have included a clue chart with each quizzle in this book. The chart will help you to record what you learn from each clue and also to record the facts that can be *deduced* by putting two or more clues together. Here is how to use the clue chart:

Suppose a clue told you: TWO BOYS HAD DIFFERENT MEATS FOR DINNER. JOHN DID NOT HAVE HAM. You would put an "x" (meaning "no") on the chart, where John's row crosses the "ham" column, like this:

	HAM	BEEF
JOHN	X	
JIM		

Now suppose the clue had told you: TWO BOYS HAD DIFFERENT MEATS. JIM HAD HAM. You would put an "O" (meaning "yes") where Jim's row crosses the "ham" column. You could also deduce from this that if Jim had the ham, John *did not*. So an "x" goes in John's "beef" box. Also, if Jim had ham, you can deduce that he did not have beef—so still another "x" goes on the chart, where the "beef" column crosses Jim's row. The remaining space gets an "O." John must have had beef!

	HAM	BEEF
JOHN	X	O
JIM	O	X

Of course, this little quizzle is so simple, it's hardly a puzzle at all. Still the principle and use of the clue chart is the same as for the more challenging quizzles in this book.

HOW TO SOLVE QUIZZLES—STEP BY STEP

Quizzles are reasoning puzzles. Each puzzle has a set-up, a set of clues, and a clue-chart to help you plot the facts as you go.

To give you the hang of it, let's solve a sample Quizzle. Here's the set-up:

DOUBLE STARS

There are five films playing in town, a comedy, a western, a thriller, a mystery, and a Sci-fi film. Each of the films stars a different leading man. They are Peter O'Toole, Dirk Bogarde, Clint Eastwood, Charlton Heston, and Laurence Olivier. As it happens, each of the films also stars a different leading lady. The female stars are Faye Dunaway, Julie Christie, Jacqueline Bisset, Liz Taylor, and Shirley MacLaine. From the clues given try to determine the male and female lead in each type of film.

Here are the clues:

1. Neither Charlton Heston nor Laurence Olivier star in the western but one stars with Jacqueline Bisset and the other with Faye Dunaway.
2. Julie Christie stars in the mystery but not with Clint Eastwood.
3. The sci-fi film does not star Jacqueline Bisset.
4. Peter O'Toole is not in a film with Shirley MacLaine and neither of them are in a mystery, sci-fi, or comedy film.
5. Charlton Heston is not in the comedy and Peter O'Toole is not in the western.

Here is the clue chart:

	COMEDY	WESTERN	THRILLER	MYSTERY	SCI-FI	DUNAWAY	CHRISTIE	BISSET	TAYLOR	MACLAINE
O'TOOLE										
BOGARDE										
EASTWOOD										
HESTON										
OLIVIER										
DUNAWAY										
CHRISTIE										
BISSET										
TAYLOR										
MACLAINE										

Let's solve this Quizzle clue by clue. We'll use the clue chart to record what we *know* and what we *deduce* from each clue.

The best attack is to take each clue in order and see what it tells you about each item in the puzzle and its relationship to other items. For instance, in clue 1, we'll learn things about Charlton Heston *and* about his relationship to two other groups of items, actresses and kinds of movies.

Look at clue 1:

1. Neither Charlton Heston nor Laurence Olivier star in the western but one stars with Jacqueline Bisset and the other with Faye Dunaway.

The clue states that Charlton Heston is *not* in a western film, so put an 'x' in the western column where it crosses the Heston row.

The clue also states that Heston stars with either Bisset or Dunaway. From this we can deduce that he *does not* star with Christie, Taylor, or MacLaine. So now we put three more 'x's on the chart, where Christie, Taylor, and MacLaine's columns cross the Heston row. We know the same about Laurence Olivier, so we can put the appropriate marks on the chart. At this point, we have charted all the *stated* facts in the clue. The chart will look like this:

	COMEDY	WESTERN	THRILLER	MYSTERY	SCI-FI	DUNAWAY	CHRISTIE	BISSET	TAYLOR	MACLAINE
O'TOOLE										
BOGARDE										
EASTWOOD										
HESTON		X					X		X	X
OLIVIER		X					X		X	X
DUNAWAY										
CHRISTIE										
BISSET										
TAYLOR										
MACLAINE										

That's all the clue tells us about Charlton Heston, so let's move on to Laurence Olivier. Like Heston, he stars with either

vi

Bisset or Dunaway, so we can assume he *does not* star with Christie, Taylor, or MacLaine. We must now put three more 'x's on the chart: where the three actress's columns cross the Olivier row. Also, like Heston, Olivier does *not* star in a western (the clue says so directly), so we put an 'x' where the Olivier row and the western column cross.

Now we must deduce some information. We have already put 'x's on the chart to show that Olivier and Heston are not in the western. We can deduce that Bisset and Dunaway cannot be in the western either — because they star with Heston and Olivier (who aren't in a western). So two more 'x's go on the chart, where the western column crosses the rows for Bisset and Dunaway.

Taking things one step further — if Bisset and Dunaway star with Heston and Olivier, then Bisset and Dunaway *do not* star with O'Toole, Bogarde, or Eastwood. So six new 'x's go on your chart — where the Bisset and Dunaway columns cross the O'Toole, Bogarde, and Eastwood rows.

See how much you learned from one simple clue? At this point, your chart should look like this:

Let's move on to clue 2:

2. Julie Christie stars in the mystery but not with Clint Eastwood.

Aha! Julie Christie stars in the mystery. That means we put an 'O' where the mystery column crosses the Julie Christie row.

If Christie stars in the mystery, the other four actresses do not — so four 'x's go in the mystery column where it crosses the rows of Dunaway, Bisset, Taylor, and MacLaine. Also, if Julie Christie stars in the mystery, we deduce that she *does not* star in any other kind of film. So four more 'x's go on the chart: where Julie Christie's row crosses the comedy, thriller, western, and sci-fi columns.

Important: whenever there is a 'O' in a space, you can put X's in the remaining spaces in that row and column within THE SQUARE.

The clue also tells us that Clint Eastwood *did not* star in the mystery with Julie Christie. That means two more 'x's: one where Eastwood's row crosses the mystery column and one where it crosses the Christie column.

Now, to get the next bit of information, we must put clues 1 and 2 together. In clue 1, we learned that Heston and Olivier did not star with Julie Christie. In clue 2, we learned that Christie starred in the mystery — THEREFORE, Heston and Olivier could not have starred in the mystery! Put the two appropriate x's on your chart. The chart will now look like this:

Clue 3 is a snap:

3. The sci-fi film does not star Jacqueline Bisset.

Just put an 'x' where the sci-fi column crosses the Bisset row.

Clue 4 is more complicated.

4. Peter O'Toole is not in a film with Shirley MacLaine and neither of them are in a mystery, sci-fi, or comedy film.

Let's start by seeing what the clue tells us about Peter O'Toole. First, he is *not* in a film with Shirley MacLaine, so we can put an 'x' where his row crosses her column. Second, he is *not* in a mystery, sci-fi, or comedy film. Three more 'x's go on the chart. Now the chart looks like this:

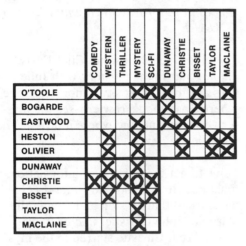

Study the chart for a moment. You will notice that all of the actor boxes in the mystery column are filled *except* for Bogarde's. That means that Bogarde is the only actor who could have starred in the mystery. So you can now put an 'O' in the mystery column where it crosses Bogarde's row.

Also, if Bogarde starred in a mystery he couldn't have starred in any other kind of film; put 'x's where the Bogarde row crosses the columns for comedy, western, sci-fi, and thriller.

At this point, the mystery column shows that Christie and Bogarde starred in the mystery. Because they appeared *together* in the mystery, you can put an 'O' where Bogarde's row crosses Christie's column. If he starred with Christie, he did *not* star with anyone else. That means two x's go where Bogarde's row crosses the Taylor and MacLaine columns. (His Dunaway and Bisset boxes are already 'x'ed from clue 1.) Likewise, the Christie column now gets an 'x' in O'Toole's row (the column's only remaining empty space). She couldn't have starred with O'Toole because she starred

with Bogarde! Now your chart should look like this:

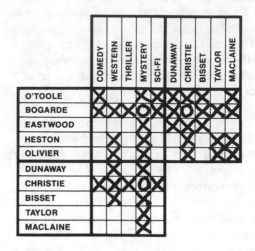

Look at the chart again—hard. Did you notice that the Shirley MacLaine column shows that she *does not* star with O'Toole, Bogarde, Heston, or Olivier, and that she has only one box left open? This means she *must have* starred with Eastwood. Put an 'O' where her column crosses his row. Put an 'x' in the remaining box of Eastwood's actress row. (If he starred with MacLaine, he *could not have* starred with anyone else).
Important: whenever there are four 'x's in a row or column WITHIN A SQUARE, you can put an 'O' in the remaining space.

Look at the chart closely again. Do you see the other hidden fact? The O'Toole row has 'X's in the Dunaway, Christie, Bisset, and MacLaine columns.

This means he can only have starred with the remaining lady — Elizabeth Taylor, the one whose box is empty in his row. Put an 'O' there.

Whenever you have an 'O', you can usually use it to deduce some new information. In this case, we just found out that O'Toole stars with Liz Taylor. Look at his row. He can only have starred in a western or a thriller. What does that tell us about Taylor? That *she* can only have starred in a western or a thriller *too*. So in Taylor's row, we can put x's in every film box *except* the western and thriller. (We already knew she did not star in the mystery.) The chart now looks like this:

	COMEDY	WESTERN	THRILLER	MYSTERY	SCI-FI	DUNAWAY	CHRISTIE	BISSET	TAYLOR	MACLAINE
O'TOOLE	X			X	X	X	X	X	O	X
BOGARDE	X	X	O			X				O
EASTWOOD		X		X	X	X	X	X		O
HESTON			X							
OLIVIER			X							
DUNAWAY										
CHRISTIE	X	X	X	O	X					
BISSET	X	X	X							
TAYLOR	X									
MACLAINE	X									

Remember Clue 4? It went like this:

4. Peter O'Toole is not in a film with Shirley MacLaine and neither of them are in a mystery, sci-fi, or comedy film.

We've already looked at this clue as it related to Peter O'Toole. Now let's see what it says about Shirley MacLaine. Simple. She was not in the mystery, sci-fi, or comedy films. So x's go in those columns, in her row. We found out a moment ago that MacLaine *stars* with Eastwood, so we can put 'x's in his mystery, sci-fi, and comedy columns too.

Now look hard and see if you can find a new piece of hidden information. Right. There is now an 'x' in every actress box of the sci-fi column *except* where it crosses Faye Dunaway's row. So put an 'O' where the Dunaway row and sci-fi column meet. Faye Dunaway was in the sci-fi film! That means she can't have been in any other kind of film, so 'x's go in the remaining film boxes in Faye's row.

If you look hard after putting in the last information, you'll see that actress boxes of the comedy column are now full, except the Jacqueline Bisset box. So Bisset was in the comedy! Put in another 'O'! Bisset can't have been in anything else, so an 'x' goes in the thriller column in Bisset's row. (That's the only open box in her film row, anyway.)

At this point, the chart should look like this:

	COMEDY	WESTERN	THRILLER	MYSTERY	SCI-FI	DUNAWAY	CHRISTIE	BISSET	TAYLOR	MACLAINE
O'TOOLE	X			X	X	X	X	X	O	X
BOGARDE	X	X	O			X	X	O		X
EASTWOOD	X	X		X	X	X	X	X		O
HESTON			X							
OLIVIER			X							
DUNAWAY	X	X	X	X	O					
CHRISTIE	X	X	X	O	X					
BISSET	O	X	X	X	X					
TAYLOR	X									
MACLAINE	X			X	X					

Now we're getting somewhere. Let's see if we can use the 'O's we just put in to dig up some new information. Dunaway is in the sci-fi and Bisset is in the comedy. We know from clue 1 (and from looking at the chart) that Heston and Olivier are in films with Dunaway and Bisset, although we still don't know who is with whom. Still, if they are with Dunaway and Bisset, who are in either the comedy or sci-fi, Heston and Olivier are in either the comedy or the sci-fi too. We have already put 'x's in the Heston and O'Toole mystery and western boxes, but now we can put 'x's in their thriller boxes as well. Why? To repeat, they're with Bisset and Dunaway — and Bisset and Dunaway are in the comedy and sci-fi, *not* in the thriller. Put in these two x's and let's move on to clue five:

5. Charlton Heston is not in the comedy and Peter O'Toole is not in the western.

Aha, again! Heston isn't in the comedy! So put an 'x' in his row in the comedy column. This leaves only Olivier to be the star of the comedy, so we can put an 'O' in the Olivier row, where it crosses the comedy column, and two 'x's where the Olivier row crosses the thriller and sci-fi columns.

Looking hard at the chart once more, we see that Heston's is now the only open box under sci-fi — so Heston is in the sci-fi film and an 'O' goes there.

We already know that Faye Dunaway is in the sci-fi film. Now we know that Heston is too. So Dunaway and Heston are together! Put an 'O' in *her* column, where it crosses his row and an 'x' where either of them crosses anyone else.

Do the same thing for Bisset and Olivier. (We just found out that Olivier is in the comedy. We already knew that Bisset is too. So Bisset and Olivier are together. Put an 'O' in her column, where it crosses his row and an 'x' where either of them crosses anyone else).

Now, your chart looks like this:

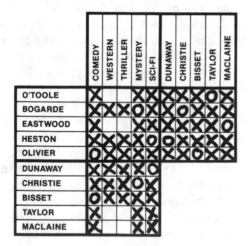

We're really down to the home stretch. All we need to know is the types of films the O'Toole-Taylor team and Eastwood MacLaine team are in. The only two types of film left are the western and the thriller. Clue 5 says in no uncertain terms that Peter O'Toole is *not* in the western. That means that O'Toole is *in the thriller.* Taylor is with O'Toole, so both get "O"s in their thriller boxes, and "X"s in the remaining boxes. This leaves the western to be the film starring Eastwood and MacLaine. Put in the appropriate "O"s — and you've solved your first Quizzle!

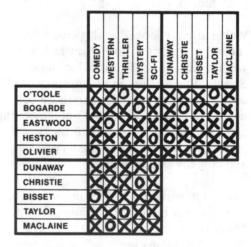

1. PROM DRESSES

Five friends, whose names are: Gail, Margery, Nora, Pamela, and Ramona, each wore a different colored dress to the senior prom. The colors of the dresses were: blue, green, orange, pink, and yellow. In alphabetical order, the last names of the five girls are: Clausen, Jensen, Mathers, Oblinski, and Smith. From the information given, determine the first and last name of each girl as well as the color of the dress that each one wore to the senior prom.

1. The girl who wore a blue dress and Ms. Mathers do not have the first name of Margery or Ramona.
2. Of Ms. Oblinski and Ms. Smith, one wore an orange dress and one is named Pamela.
3. Margery is not Ms. Smith and she did not wear a pink dress.
4. Nora, Pamela, and Ms. Clausen did not wear a blue or orange dress.
5. Of Gail and Pamela, one is Ms. Jensen and one wore a green dress.

	CLAUSEN	JENSEN	MATHERS	OBLINSKI	SMITH	BLUE	GREEN	ORANGE	PINK	YELLOW
GAIL										
MARGERY										
NORA										
PAMELA										
RAMONA										
BLUE					
GREEN					
ORANGE					
PINK					
YELLOW					

1

2. DOUBLE GIFTS

Five women went shopping together to get birthday presents for a mutual friend. Their names are: Nancy, Olivia, Rita, Sally, and Vivian. The five gifts that they bought for their friend are: gloves, a necklace, a sweater, a wallet, and a watch. While shopping each woman bought one of the same gifts for herself. From the information given, determine the gift that each woman bought for her friend as well as the gift that each one bought for herself.

1. Nancy and Rita did not buy a sweater or a wallet.
2. Vivian bought a necklace for herself and the woman who bought the same gift for her friend is not Rita.
3. Sally bought for herself the same thing that Olivia bought for her friend.
4. Vivian and Rita bought watches.
5. Sally did not buy a sweater for herself.

	FOR SELF					FOR FRIEND				
	GLOVES	NECKLACE	SWEATER	WALLET	WATCH	GLOVES	NECKLACE	SWEATER	WALLET	WATCH
NANCY										
OLIVIA										
RITA										
SALLY										
VIVIAN										
FOR FRIEND GLOVES					
NECKLACE					
SWEATER					
WALLET					
WATCH					

3. TEST CARS' MPG'S

The miles-per-gallon ratings on a single model of a car may vary for many reasons, including the test driver and other factors. A new model line of popular car called the Zinx, during tests, produced mpg's of 32, 31, 30, 29, and 28. Each car was a different one of these five colors: blue, green, red, white, and yellow. Each car was driven by a different one of these five drivers: Cox, Durham, Gosling, Heynek, and Wollinsky. From the information given, determine the color and driver of each car, as well as the mpg attained by each one.

1. The driver named Durham got more mpg's than the green car but not as many as the red car.
2. The blue car got better mpg's than the car driven by Wollinsky.
3. Cox did not drive the green or red car.
4. The yellow car got more mpg's than the car driven by Gosling but not as many as the green car.

	BLUE	GREEN	RED	WHITE	YELLOW	COX	DURHAM	GOSLING	HEYNEK	WOLLINSKY
32 MPG										
31 MPG										
30 MPG										
29 MPG										
28 MPG										
COX										
DURHAM										
GOSLING										
HEYNEK										
WOLLINSKY										

4. BANK EMPLOYEES

Sometimes people are perfect for their jobs. In the case of five employees of the Tinyboro bank this is very much the case. The five employees are named: Cash, Coyne, El Grande, Finn, and Nicholson. In alphabetical order their names are: Bill, Buck, Nick, Penny, and Senta. The positions that they hold at the bank are as a head teller, an officer, the president, a security guard, and a teller. From the information given, determine the first and last name of each employee and the position each holds at the bank.

1. The president is a man but neither he nor Buck has the last name of El Grande, Finn, or Nicholson.
2. Senta's last name is not Finn and neither of these two is the security guard.
3. The two tellers are not the same sex but one is named Nicholson and one is named Coyne.
4. Buck and Mr. Cash are not the regular teller.
5. Neither Penny nor Mr. El Grande is the president.

	BILL	BUCK	NICK	PENNY	SENTA	CASH	COYNE	EL GRANDE	FINN	NICHOLSON
HEAD TELLER										
OFFICER										
PRESIDENT										
SEC. GUARD										
TELLER										
CASH										
COYNE										
EL GRANDE										
FINN										
NICHOLSON										

5. BASEBALL-HITTING CONTEST

In a baseball-hitting contest at the office picnic, five men participated named: Biff, Carl, Fred, Marty, and Tom. Their last names, in alphabetical order, are: Jenkins, Keech, MacNab, Miller, and Winslow. The distances that each man hit the ball in feet are: 325, 300, 275, 250, and 200. From the information given, determine the first and last name of each man, as well as how far each one hit the baseball.

1. Mr. Miller didn't hit the ball as far as Biff, but he hit one farther than Tom.
2. Carl hit the ball farther than Marty, but not the farthest.
3. Fred hit a ball farther than Mr. MacNab but not as far as Mr. Keech, who didn't hit the ball the farthest.
4. Tom hit a ball farther than Mr. Winslow, whose first name is not Marty.

	BIFF	CARL	FRED	MARTY	TOM	JENKINS	KEECH	MAC NAB	MILLER	WINSLOW
325										
300										
275										
250										
200										
JENKINS										
KEECH										
MAC NAB										
MILLER										
WINSLOW										

6. CANDIDATES

The five candidates for mayor in the town of Smallville were members of these five parties: Conservative, Democrat, Independent, Liberal, and Republican. Their names are: Goshen, Hargreaves, Jensen, Liebowitz, and Nelson. From the information given, determine not only the party to which each of the candidates belong, but also the order of finish in the election.

1. The Democrat and the Independent, in no particular order, were the first- and fifth-place vote-getters, but neither one is named Hargreaves or Jensen.
2. Nelson did better than Liebowitz but not as well as the Republican.
3. Goshen is not an Independent candidate.
4. The Liberal did better than Jensen but not as well as Hargreaves.

	CONSERVATIVE	DEMOCRAT	INDEPENDENT	LIBERAL	REPUBLICAN	GOSHEN	HARGREAVES	JENSEN	LIEBOWITZ	NELSON
FIRST										
SECOND										
THIRD										
FOURTH										
FIFTH										
GOSHEN										
HARGREAVES										
JENSEN										
LIEBOWITZ										
NELSON										

7. BIRTHDAYS IN JUNE

All of Ms. Johnson's children were born in June. Their birthdays are: June 1, June 7, June 12, June 20, and June 29. There are three girls named Mary, Elvira, and Joan, and there are two boys named Douglas and Timothy. She bought these five presents for them: a book, a coat, concert tickets, a dress, and an electronic game. From the information given, determine the birthday and present received by each child.

1. Timothy's birthday comes before that of the girl who received a dress but after the girl who received a coat.
2. Douglas's birthday comes before Elvira's birthday but after the birthday of the girl who received an electronic game.
3. Elvira did not receive the dress and neither did Joan.
4. Douglas did not get a book as a present.

	DOUGLAS	ELVIRA	JOAN	MARY	TIMOTHY	BOOK	COAT	CONCERT TIX	DRESS	ELEC. GAME
JUNE 1										
JUNE 7										
JUNE 12										
JUNE 20										
JUNE 29										
BOOK										
COAT										
CONCERT TIX										
DRESS										
ELEC. GAME										

8. WIN, PLACE, AND SHOW PLUS TWO

In the big race at the Horseheads' racetrack the top five finishers were: Full Sweep, Nightshade, Quartermain, Top Drawer, and Whirlaway. In alphabetical order, they were ridden by: Alvarez, Hernandez, Perez, Pickman, and Wilson. From the information given, determine the order of finish of the race and the name of the jockey who rode each of the five horses.

1. Of Whirlaway and Quartermain, one finished first and one was ridden by Alvarez.
2. Pickman finished ahead of Perez but after Whirlaway.
3. Full Sweep did not finish third.
4. Top Drawer finished ahead of Nightshade but after Wilson, who did not ride the winning horse.

	FULL SWEEP	NIGHTSHADE	QUARTERMAIN	TOP DRAWER	WHIRLAWAY	ALVAREZ	HERNANDEZ	PEREZ	PICKMAN	WILSON
FIRST										
SECOND										
THIRD										
FOURTH										
FIFTH										
ALVAREZ										
HERNANDEZ										
PEREZ										
PICKMAN										
WILSON										

9. B-BALL PLAYERS

Bill, Ernie, Oscar, Sammy, and Tony are the five basketball players on the starting team of the varsity squad. Each one is known by a different one of these five nicknames: Slats, Stretch, Tiny, Tower, and Tree. From the information given, determine the nickname of each player as well as each of their heights, whether 6'6", 6'5", 6'3", 6'1", or 6' tall.

1. Oscar is taller than Tree who is taller than Tony.
2. Bill is taller than Sammy but shorter than Slats.
3. Tony's nickname is not Tiny.
4. Stretch is taller than Oscar but not the tallest.

	SLATS	STRETCH	TINY	TOWER	TREE	BILL	ERNIE	OSCAR	SAMMY	TONY
6'6"										
6'5"										
6'3"										
6'1"										
6'										
BILL										
ERNIE										
OSCAR										
SAMMY										
TONY										

Five eye doctors named Harlon, Harry, Henry, Herbert, and Horace operate an eye clinic. They each have one of these five unusual names: Eismann, Frayme, Glassman, Lenz, and Rimbaud. They each wear a different type of glasses from among these five: bifocals, contact lenses, reading glasses, regular glasses, and tinted lenses. From the information given, determine the first and last name of each man as well as the type of glasses worn.

1. Harry is not Mr. Glassman and he doesn't wear reading glasses.
2. Henry, Herbert, and Mr. Lenz do not wear bifocals or regular glasses.
3. Of Harlon and Herbert, one is named Eismann and one wears tinted lenses.
4. The man who wears bifocals and Mr. Rimbaud are not named Harry or Horace.
5. Of Mr. Frayme and Mr. Glassman, one is named Herbert and one wears regular glasses.

	EISMANN	FRAYME	GLASSMAN	LENZ	RIMBAUD	BIFOCALS	CONTACTS	READING	REGULAR	TINTED
HARLON										
HARRY										
HENRY										
HERBERT										
HORACE										
BIFOCALS					
CONTACTS					
READ. GLASSES					
REG. GLASSES					
TINTED LENSES					

11. WHERE ARE THE KIDS AT 11 P.M.?

The Johnson kids are each upstairs in their bedrooms at 11 P.M., however, each one is doing something different, either: doing crossword puzzles, drawing, reading, sleeping, or watching TV. The five kids are three boys named Albert, Daniel, and Ryan, and two girls named Cathy and Grace. They range in age from 14 to 18 years old. From the information given, determine each child's age and what he or she is doing at 11 P.M.

1. The eldest, a daughter, is not watching TV, or sleeping.
2. Grace is not reading or watching TV.
3. The child who is drawing is older than Grace but younger than Daniel.
4. The child who is reading is younger than Ryan but older than Albert.

	ALBERT	CATHY	DANIEL	GRACE	RYAN	CROSSWORDS	DRAWING	READING	SLEEPING	T.V.
18										
17										
16										
15										
14										
CROSSWORDS					
DRAWING					
READING					
SLEEPING					
T.V.					

12. FORKS IN THE ROAD

There are five forks in the road from Tratsburg to Denville. Turning left at each of these five forks will lead to one of these five towns: Asterly, Hornton, Seattle, Teasdale, and Thornton. Turning right at each of the five forks will lead to one of these five towns: Estwater, Houston, Stewartville, Tewsbury, and Thousand Oaks. From the information given, determine the left and right turning at each fork in the road, as well as the order that a traveler would come upon the five forks heading from Tratsburg to Denville.

1. The fork in the road to Houston comes earlier than the one to Tewsbury but later than the ones to Teasdale or Thornberry, but neither of these two is a turning at the first fork in the road.
2. There is not a fork with roads to Stewartville and Asterly.
3. The fork with a road to Thousand Oaks comes before the one to Teasdale, but after the one to Stewartville.
4. The fork to Hornton is not at the same place as the one to Stewartville or Tewsbury.

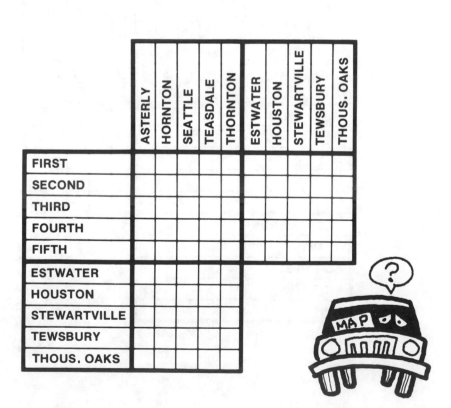

	ASTERLY	HORNTON	SEATTLE	TEASDALE	THORNTON	ESTWATER	HOUSTON	STEWARTVILLE	TEWSBURY	THOUS. OAKS
FIRST										
SECOND										
THIRD										
FOURTH										
FIFTH										
ESTWATER										
HOUSTON										
STEWARTVILLE										
TEWSBURY										
THOUS. OAKS										

13. WINTER VACATIONS

Lucky Duckworth and his wife took five vacations last winter, one in each of the months of: November, December, January, February, and March. Each vacation was for a different length of time, either: two weeks, one week, five days, four days, or three days. They went to these five places: Bermuda, Hawaii, Jamaica, Puerto Rico, and Tahiti. From the information given, determine where they went on vacation each month and how long they stayed.

1. Their two longest vacations were in the Pacific but neither of these two longest vacations were in November or March.
2. They did not go to Puerto Rico for four days.
3. They went on a five-day vacation before going to Bermuda but after going to Puerto Rico.
4. The January vacation was longer and after the Tahitian vacation but before their vacation to Jamaica.

	TWO WEEKS	ONE WEEK	FIVE DAYS	FOUR DAYS	THREE DAYS	BERMUDA	HAWAII	JAMAICA	PUERTO RICO	TAHITI
NOVEMBER										
DECEMBER										
JANUARY										
FEBRUARY										
MARCH										
BERMUDA										
HAWAII										
JAMAICA										
PUERTO RICO										
TAHITI										

14. TOP LOCAL STATIONS

The five top local radio stations in the town of Medio are: WIGT, WKCK, WLTR, WTBG, and WWZZ. Each station plays a different one of these five types of music: classical, country, jazz, muzak, and rock. From the information given, determine the type of music played on each station as well as its ranking in popularity from one to five.

1. WKCK ranked higher than the jazz station but lower than the station that plays muzak.
2. WTBG does not play rock or classical music.
3. The classical station ranked lower than WLTR.
4. WTBG ranked higher than the station that plays muzak but lower than WWZZ.

	WIGT	WKCK	WLTR	WTBG	WWZZ	CLASSICAL	COUNTRY	JAZZ	MUZAK	ROCK
1										
2										
3										
4										
5										
CLASSICAL					
COUNTRY					
JAZZ					
MUZAK					
ROCK					

15. CB'ERS

The "handles" of five cb'ers are: All 'Round Guy, Big Daddy, Hot Wheels, Lightning, and Shifty. In alphabetical order their real names are: Al, Gus, Herb, Ken, and Pete. They are each a different one of these five occupations: delivery man, realtor, repairman, salesman, and trucker. From the information given, determine each man's "handle" and occupation.

1. The salesman is not Pete or Ken and neither of these three is called Shifty.
2. The realtor is not named Al or Pete and neither of these three goes by the "handle" of All 'Round Guy or Shifty.
3. Big Daddy is not the "handle" of Pete or the realtor.
4. Of Ken and Herb, one is the trucker and one is named Hot Wheels.
5. Of the salesman and the repairman, one is Gus and one goes by the "handle" of Lightning.

	AL	GUS	HERB	KEN	PETE	DELIVERY MAN	REALTOR	REPAIRMAN	SALESMAN	TRUCKER
GUY										
BIG DADDY										
HOT WHEELS										
LIGHTNING										
SHIFTY										
DELIVERY MAN										
REALTOR										
REPAIRMAN										
SALESMAN										
TRUCKER										

16. CAR POOL

Three men named Greene, Grey, and Tann, along with two women named Browne and Whyte, each drive the car in their car pool on a different one of the five weekdays each week. Each person's car is a different one of these five colors: brown, gray, green, tan, and white. From the information given, determine the day on which each person drives, as well as the color of his or her car.

1. The color of no person's car is similar to his or her name.
2. They ride in the green car earlier in the week than in the tan car but later than in the gray car.
3. The woman who drives the brown car drives later in the week than Mr. Greene but earlier than Mr. Grey, who is not the man who drives on Friday.
4. The man who drives the tan car drives earlier in the week than the man who drives the white car but later than Ms. Browne, who does not drive on Monday.
5. Ms. Browne does not drive on Tuesday.

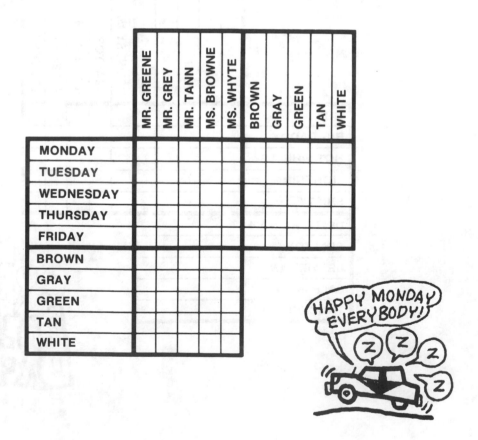

17. BAY AREA MYSTERIES

Sam Chovell is a private detective working in the Bay Area. One month he helped the police to solve five mysteries. The crimes involved were: arson, embezzlement, kidnapping, murder, and robbery. Each of the crimes occurred in a different one of these five cities: Berkeley, Oakland, Palo Alto, San Francisco, and San Jose. The primary clue that he used to solve the crime was different in each case, either an eyewitness, fingerprints, a letter, a phone tip, or a tire track. From the information given, determine the location of each type of crime as well as the type of clue that cracked each case.

1. In no particular order, the mysteries solved in Berkeley, Oakland, and Palo Alto were arson, embezzlement, and the one solved by the evidence of an eyewitness.
2. The tire track and the phone tip were not the clues that solved the crimes of embezzlement or murder.
3. The murder, the kidnapping, and the crime solved by the clue in a letter did not occur in San Jose or Palo Alto.
4. The crime solved by a tire-track clue, the kidnapping, and the robbery did not occur in San Francisco.
5. The crime in Berkeley was not solved by a clue found in a letter.

	ARSON	EMBEZZLE	KIDNAPPING	MURDER	ROBBERY	EYEWITNESS	FINGERPRINTS	LETTER	PHONE TIP	TIRE TRACK
BERKELEY										
OAKLAND										
PALO ALTO										
SAN FRAN.										
SAN JOSE										
EYEWITNESS										
FINGERPRINTS										
LETTER										
PHONE TIP										
TIRE TRACK										

18. COMMUTERS

Five employees at the Wild Fowl Publishing Company each come to work by a different one of these five means: bus, car, railroad, subway, and walking. They hold these five positions at the company: art director, editor, publisher, receptionist, and secretary. Two of them are men named Finch and Marten, while three of them are women named Fulmer, Gannet, and Hawk. From the information given, determine the position held by each person as well as the means by which each one gets to work each day.

1. Neither of the men walk to work but one is the art director and the other is not the publisher or secretary.
2. The publisher is not named Hawk or Fulmer and none of these three takes the railroad or a car.
3. Mr. Finch does not come by railroad and he is not the editor.
4. The female receptionist is not named Fulmer and neither of these two walks to work.
5. The secretary does not take the bus to work.

	BUS	CAR	RAILROAD	SUBWAY	WALK	ART DIRECTOR	EDITOR	PUBLISHER	RECEPTIONIST	SECRETARY
MR. FINCH										
MR. MARTEN										
MS. FULMER										
MS. GANNET										
MS. HAWK										
ART DIRECTOR										
EDITOR										
PUBLISHER										
RECEPTIONIST										
SECRETARY										

19. POPULAR NEW SECRETARY

A popular new secretary at the law firm of Farnsworth, Newman, O'Malley, Price, and Reynolds, is taken to lunch by a different one of those five men on each of the five days of her first week on the job. Each man took her to eat a different one of these five types of food: Chinese, French, Greek, Indian, and Mexican. From the information given, determine whom she went to lunch with on each day and the type of food that they had.

1. Neither Mr. Newman nor Mr. Reynolds took her to lunch on Thursday or Friday but one took her for Chinese food and the one who took her to lunch earlier than the other took her for Greek food.
2. She went for a Mexican food lunch before her Indian food lunch but after her lunch with Mr. Price.
3. She had lunch with Mr. Farnsworth before her lunch with Mr. O'Malley but after the lunch when she had French food, which was not on Monday.
4. She had lunch with Mr. Newman later in the week than the lunch when she had French food.

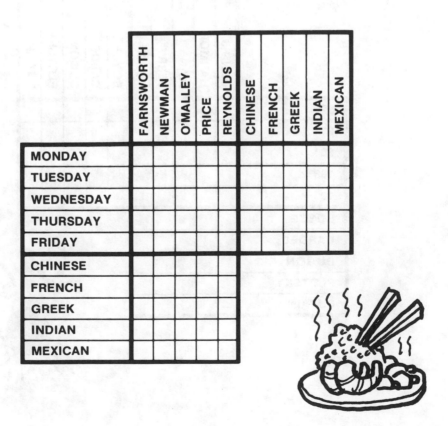

	FARNSWORTH	NEWMAN	O'MALLEY	PRICE	REYNOLDS	CHINESE	FRENCH	GREEK	INDIAN	MEXICAN
MONDAY										
TUESDAY										
WEDNESDAY										
THURSDAY										
FRIDAY										
CHINESE										
FRENCH										
GREEK										
INDIAN										
MEXICAN										

The averages of the five men on the Brewery bowling team are 220, 211, 201, 198, and 195. The men are named: Dennis, Harmon, Ivan, Jerry, and Willie. In alphabetical order their last names are: Boyce, Cardel, Dugon, Plotsky, and Sutain. From the information given, determine each man's first and last name as well as his bowling average.

1. Of Harmon and Mr. Plotsky, one has the highest average and one has the lowest average.
2. Jerry's average is lower than that of Mr. Sutain but not the lowest.
3. Harmon is not Mr. Boyce.
4. Mr. Dugon is not named Willie but his average is higher than Mr. Sutain's and lower than Ivan's average.

	DENNIS	HARMON	IVAN	JERRY	WILLIE	BOYCE	CARDEL	DUGON	PLOTSKY	SUTAIN
220										
211										
201										
198										
195										
BOYCE										
CARDEL										
DUGON										
PLOTSKY										
SUTAIN										

21. ANTIQUE SHOPPING

Five women friends went antique shopping together in the old section of town. Their names are Addison, Comisky, Evans, Simmons, and Wallis. They each bought a different one of these five items: chair, desk, lamp, stool, and vase. The items ranged in price from $100.00 to $500.00. From the information given, determine the object bought by each woman as well as its price.

1. The chair cost less than what Ms. Addison bought but more than what Ms. Wallis bought.
2. The item bought by Ms. Simmons cost more than the item bought by Ms. Evans but less than the lamp.
3. Ms. Comisky bought something that cost more than the lamp but it was not the desk.
4. The vase cost less than the desk but more than the stool.

	ADDISON	COMISKY	EVANS	SIMMONS	WALLIS	CHAIR	DESK	LAMP	STOOL	VASE
$500.00										
$400.00										
$300.00										
$200.00										
$100.00										
CHAIR										
DESK										
LAMP										
STOOL										
VASE										

$100 to $500

22. SISTER CITIES

The five cities of Appleboro, Bellville, Cherryvale, Keystown, and Peachburg have each adopted a sister city abroad. Those five cities are: Abbemount, Corley, Monmouth, Newton, and Poulson. Each city is located in a different one of these five foreign countries: Australia, Canada, Great Britain, New Zealand, and South Africa. From the information given, determine the name and country location of the sister city of each of the five American towns.

1. Of Corley and Monmouth, one is in New Zealand and one is in Australia but neither one is the sister city of Appleboro, Bellville, or Peachburg.
2. Newton is not in Great Britain.
3. Of Appleboro and Keystown, one is the sister city of a city in Canada and one is the sister city of the city of Monmouth.
4. The sister city of Bellville, the sister city of Cherryvale, and Poulson are not in either New Zealand or South Africa.

	ABBEMOUNT	CORLEY	MONMOUTH	NEWTON	POULSON	AUSTRALIA	CANADA	GREAT BRITAIN	NEW ZEALAND	SOUTH AFRICA
APPLEBORO										
BELLVILLE										
CHERRYVALE										
KEYSTOWN										
PEACHBURG										
AUSTRALIA					
CANADA					
GREAT BRITAIN					
NEW ZEALAND					
SOUTH AFRICA					

23. WHERE ARE THEY NOW?

Five college friends got together for the wedding of an old, mutual friend. Their current occupations are: artist, banker, diplomat, florist, and lawyer. Each one currently resides in a different one of these five cities: Cairo (Egypt), Los Angeles, Paris (France), Philadelphia, and Zurich (Switzerland). The two men are named Silver and White, while the three women are named Black, Brown, and Green. From the information given, determine the current occupation and place of residence of each of the five friends.

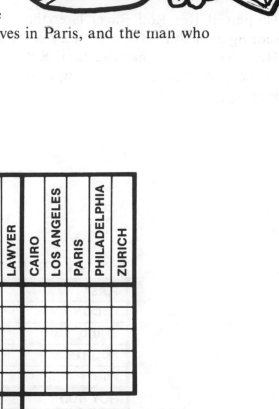

1. Ms. Black does not live in Cairo and she is not the woman artist.
2. Ms. Brown and the diplomat live outside of the U.S. but not in Zurich.
3. The five friends are: Ms. Black, Mr. White, the lawyer (who lives in the U.S.), the woman who lives in Paris, and the man who lives in L.A.
4. Mr. Silver is not the banker.

	ARTIST	BANKER	DIPLOMAT	FLORIST	LAWYER	CAIRO	LOS ANGELES	PARIS	PHILADELPHIA	ZURICH
MR. SILVER										
MR. WHITE										
MS. BLACK										
MS. BROWN										
MS. GREEN										
CAIRO										
LOS ANGELES										
PARIS										
PHILADELPHIA										
ZURICH										

CONGRATS!

24. VIDEO WIZARD

John (Joystick) Jones spends a great deal of his time in the arcades playing his five favorite video games: Hot Rod Racer, Mazerama, Pool Shark, Robot Blaster, and Space Wars. One time he played each of the five games once and achieved these scores: 250,000, 200,000, 150,000, 100,000, and 50,000 points. From the information given, determine the order in which he played the five games and the scores achieved on each one.

1. His first game, his last game, and Space Wars were not the games on which he got his highest or lowest scores.
2. He got a higher score on Robot Blaster than on Pool Shark but a lower score than on Space Wars.
3. He played Hot Rod Racer later than his highest scoring game but earlier than his second-highest scoring game.
4. He played Mazerama later than Robot Blaster but earlier than Pool Shark; one of these was his highest scoring game but neither of the other two was his lowest scoring game.

	250,000	200,000	150,000	100,000	50,000	HOT ROD	MAZERAMA	POOL SHARK	BLASTER	SPACE WARS
FIRST										
SECOND										
THIRD										
FOURTH										
FIFTH										
HOT ROD										
MAZERAMA										
POOL SHARK										
BLASTER										
SPACE WARS										

25. DIVORCE

The marriages of five brothers ended in divorce after various numbers of years married. The five brothers are named: James, Jeremy, John, Joseph, and Justin. Their five wives are named: Bertrice, Loreen, Luanne, Maybelle, and Rosette. From the information given, determine the name of each brother's wife as well as the number of years that each was married. All five couples were married on the same day.

1. Although Justin was married for half as long as Luanne, he was married one year longer than Jeremy, who was married for half as long as Rosette—none of these people are husband and wife.
2. Ten years was the longest marriage.
3. Loreen was married one year longer than Joseph but one year less than Justin.
4. James was not married to Maybelle and neither of them was a part of the couple who were the first or last to get divorced.

		JAMES	JEREMY	JOHN	JOSEPH	JUSTIN	BERTRICE	LOREEN	LUANNE	MAYBELLE	ROSETTE
YEARS MARRIED	MOST										
	LEAST										
BERTRICE											
LOREEN											
LUANNE											
MAYBELLE											
ROSETTE											

The final standings at the end of the Little League
season put these five teams in the top five positions:
Bobcats, Cougars, Lions, Panthers, and Tigers.
Each team is sponsored by a different one of these
local businesses: Al's Hardware, City Bank, Decker
Insurance Company, Joe's Florist, and Mom's
Bakery. From the information given, determine the
name and sponsor of each team and how they
finished in the standings.

1. The Panthers finished higher in the standings
   than the City Bank team.
2. Al's Hardware team is not called the Lions and
   the team sponsored by Mom's Bakery is not
   called the Bobcats.
3. The Decker Insurance Company team did not do
   as well as the Lions but they did better than the
   Cougars who did not finish in fifth place.
4. The Tigers finished higher in the standings than the team sponsored by Mom's
   Bakery but lower than the team sponsored by Joe's Florist which is not the team
   that finished first.

	BOBCATS	COUGARS	LIONS	PANTHERS	TIGERS	HARDWARE	CITY BANK	DECKER INS.	JOE'S FLORIST	MOM'S BAKERY
FIRST										
SECOND										
THIRD										
FOURTH										
FIFTH										
HARDWARE										
CITY BANK										
DECKER INS.										
JOE'S FLORIST										
MOM'S BAKERY										

27. CHOICE OF SHOWS

The Gold Dust, Gold Horn, Gold Rush, Silver Bell, and Silver Dollar are five popular showplaces on the strip. At each club one week a different one of these five singers was performing: Carol Channing, Tom Jones, Liza Minnelli, Wayne Newton, and Andy Williams. Opening the show for each of them was a different one of these five comics: David Brenner, George Carlin, Gilda Radner, Joan Rivers, and Lily Tomlin. From the information given, determine the singer and comic performing at each club.

1. The only place where the performers are both women is the Gold Rush and the only place where the performers are both men is the Gold Horn.
2. Brenner and Tomlin are appearing in places whose names have "Silver" in them, but Channing is not.
3. The male comic appearing with Newton is not Brenner.
4. The male singer appearing with Radner is not Williams and neither of them is appearing at the Silver Bell.

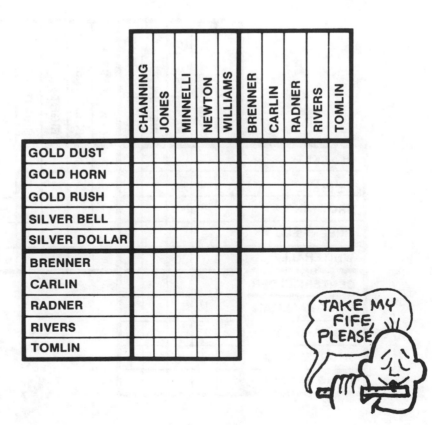

	CHANNING	JONES	MINNELLI	NEWTON	WILLIAMS	BRENNER	CARLIN	RADNER	RIVERS	TOMLIN
GOLD DUST										
GOLD HORN										
GOLD RUSH										
SILVER BELL										
SILVER DOLLAR										
BRENNER										
CARLIN										
RADNER										
RIVERS										
TOMLIN										

TAKE MY FIFE, PLEASE

28. LUCKY CHARMS

Baseball players are notoriously superstitious. Blacket, Bluet, Browning, Greenfield, and Whitehall are five players on the Boomtown Bombers who each carry a different lucky charm with them in every game. The charms are: a four-leaf clover, a penny, a rabbit's foot, a ribbon, and a silver dollar. The five positions that they play are: centerfield, first base, right field, shortstop, and third base. From the information given, determine each player's lucky charm as well as his position.

1. Neither Browning nor the two outfielders have a coin as a lucky charm.
2. Bluet is not an outfielder.
3. Greenfield is an outfielder and Whitehall's infield position is not first base but neither has his lucky charm a clover or a penny and Blacket does not have either of these two lucky charms.
4. Blacket and Bluet are not the players who play first base or third base and neither of them has a lucky ribbon.
5. The centerfielder's lucky charm is not a rabbit's foot.

	CLOVER	PENNY	RABBIT'S FOOT	RIBBON	SILVER DOLLAR	CENTERFIELDER	FIRST BASEMAN	RIGHT FIELDER	SHORTSTOP	THIRD BASEMAN
BLACKET										
BLUET										
BROWNING										
GREENFIELD										
WHITEHALL										
CENTERFIELDER					
FIRST BASEMAN					
RIGHT FIELDER					
SHORTSTOP					
THIRD BASEMAN					

29. WEARING OF THE GREEN

Five Irish-Americans each wore a different article of green clothing on St. Patrick's Day: hat, scarf, shirt, tie, and trousers. The five men are named: Brian, Francis, Frank, Liam, and Mike. No man has the same first and last initial, and the last names are: Brady, Flanagan, Lynch, Maguire, and Murphy. From the information given, determine each man's first and last name as well as the article of green clothing that he wore on St. Patrick's Day.

1. Francis and Mr. Maguire did not wear a green shirt.
2. Mr. Flanagan, Mr. Maguire, and Brian did not wear a green hat or scarf.
3. Mike, Liam, and Mr. Brady did not wear a green shirt or tie.
4. Mike is not Mr. Flanagan and neither wore a green scarf.

	BRADY	FLANAGAN	LYNCH	MAGUIRE	MURPHY	HAT	SCARF	SHIRT	TIE	TROUSERS
BRIAN										
FRANCIS										
FRANK										
LIAM										
MIKE										
HAT										
SCARF										
SHIRT										
TIE										
TROUSERS										

30. RUBIK'S CUBE CONTEST

The six top finishers in a Rubik's cube contest solved the cube is 0:29, 0:35, 0:51, 1:10, 1:26, and 1:30. Each started by completing a top color. Each one chose a different color to start with: blue, green, orange, red, white, and yellow. Of the six, three were boys named Eric, Oswald, and Wilbur, and three were girls named Gretchen, Lily, and Wendy. From the information given, determine how long it took for each one to solve the cube and what color each one used as a top starting color.

1. Gretchen's time was faster than Lily's time but slower than Eric's time; these three kids, like the girl who won the contest, did not begin with orange or green on top.
2. The girl who starts with red finished later than the kid who starts with orange but earlier than the girl who starts with blue.
3. The kid who starts with yellow on top finished earlier than Wilbur but not first.
4. Lily finished the cube earlier than Oswald.

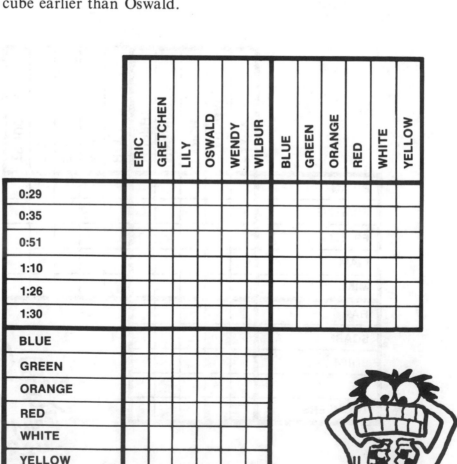

	ERIC	GRETCHEN	LILY	OSWALD	WENDY	WILBUR	BLUE	GREEN	ORANGE	RED	WHITE	YELLOW
0:29												
0:35												
0:51												
1:10												
1:26												
1:30												
BLUE												
GREEN												
ORANGE												
RED												
WHITE												
YELLOW												

In order to make time during the long ride back to school, five friends traveling in the same car only made one stop, at which time they got gas, had lunch, and used the men's room. When they got back into the car each took a different seat, including the driver, than they had occupied during the first half of the journey. From the information given, determine where Bruce, Jacob, Neil, Oscar, and Sanford sat during the two halves of the journey.

1. Only one of the five guys was in the front seat of the car for both halves of the trip.
2. At the stop Oscar switched from the back to the front and Sanford switched from the front to the back.
3. Jacob and Neil switched positions.
4. The person who drove for the second half of the trip had been sitting in the center in the back for the first half of the trip at which time Neil was not sitting on his right.

	FIRST HALF					SECOND HALF				
	CENTER REAR	DRIVER	FRONT PASS.	LEFT REAR	RIGHT REAR	CENTER REAR	DRIVER	FRONT PASS.	LEFT REAR	RIGHT REAR
BRUCE										
JACOB										
NEIL										
OSCAR										
SANFORD										
SECOND HALF — CENTER REAR										
SECOND HALF — DRIVER										
SECOND HALF — FRONT PASS.										
SECOND HALF — LEFT REAR										
SECOND HALF — RIGHT REAR										

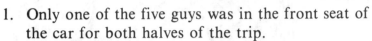

32. COUNTRY FAIR

The carnival was in town for the week and five friends spent many evenings there. They are two boys named Carl and Clark, and three girls named Carol, Clara, and Clare. They each had a favorite ride at the carnival, either the dodgems, ferris wheel, round-up scrambler, or whip. They also liked to spend time in the midway trying to win prizes at their favorite booths. Each had a different favorite booth: baseball throw, darts, horse racing, ring toss, and sledge hammer. From the information given, determine the favorite ride and midway attraction of each of the five friends.

1. One boy likes throwing baseballs and the other boy likes riding the whip.
2. The girl who likes the dodgems and the girl who likes the ring toss are not named Clara.
3. Carl does not like the round-up and his favorite contest is not darts or the horse race.
4. Carol is not the girl who likes the ferris wheel or the girl who likes the scrambler and Carol's favorite contest is not darts or ring toss.
5. Clare's favorite ride is not the ferris wheel.

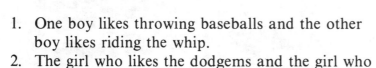

	BASEBALL	DARTS	HORSE RACE	RING TOSS	HAMMER	DODGEMS	FERRIS WHEEL	ROUND-UP	SCRAMBLER	WHIP
CARL										
CAROL										
CLARA										
CLARE										
CLARK										
DODGEMS										
FERRIS WHEEL										
ROUND-UP										
SCRAMBLER										
WHIP										

Three women named Brewster, Desmond, and Farrell along with two men named Donahue and Hendricks are all staying on the ninth floor of the Dawnlight Hotel. They have each left a wake-up call with the desk clerk for a different time in the morning: either 7:00, 7:15, 7:20, or 7:45. Their room numbers are: 945, 930, 920, 915, and 900. From the information given, determine each person's room number and the time each one wishes to be called in the morning.

1. A woman has the highest room number and a man has the lowest room number but neither wishes to be awakened at 7:00 or 7:45.
2. The woman in room 915 wishes to be called earlier than the man in room 930 but later than Ms. Farrell who is not the woman who wishes to be called before everybody else.
3. Ms. Brewster's room number is lower than the room number of the person who wishes to be called first.
4. Mr. Donahue's room number is lower than Ms. Brewster's room number and he wishes to be called later than she.

	BREWSTER	DESMOND	DONAHUE	FARRELL	HENDRICKS	945	930	920	915	900
7:00										
7:15										
7:20										
7:30										
7:45										
945										
930										
920										
915										
900										

34. FISH-RAISING KIDS

Five friends each enjoy raising tropical fish. They each have a different one of these size tanks: 50 gallons, 30 gallons, 25 gallons, 20 gallons, and 10 gallons. There are three boys named Arthur, Martin, and Maurice as well as two girls named Alice and Maureen. They each raise a different one of these types of fish: angelfish, cichlids, gouramis, guppies, and neon tetras. From the information given, determine the size of each person's tank and the type of fish raised.

1. Neither Martin nor Alice raise neon tetras and the same is true of the other two kids; who are the girl with the largest tank of all and the boy with the smallest tank of all.
2. Maurice does not raise gouramis.
3. Arthur's tank is larger than the tank in which angelfish are raised which is not the smallest tank.
4. Martin has a smaller tank than the kid who raises cichlids but a larger one than the tank in which neon tetras are raised.

	ALICE	ARTHUR	MARTIN	MAUREEN	MAURICE	ANGELFISH	CICHLIDS	GOURAMIS	GUPPIES	NEON TETRAS
50 GAL.										
30 GAL.										
25 GAL.										
20 GAL.										
10 GAL.										
ANGELFISH					
CICHLIDS					
GOURAMIS					
GUPPIES					
NEON TETRAS					

PIRANHA

NICE KITTY KITTY

The first choice and second choice in a popular book club for the months January through May were: mysteries, romances, science fiction, thrillers, and westerns. From the information given, determine the first and second choice offered by the club for each month.

1. In no single month were the first and second choices both the same type of book and in no two months were the first and second choices the same two types of books in reverse order.
2. In January and May neither the first nor the second choice was a western or a mystery.
3. A mystery was offered as the second choice earlier in the year than the month in which a mystery was offered as a first choice but later in the year than the month in which a western was offered as a first choice.
4. A romance novel was offered as a second choice earlier than a romance novel was offered as a first choice but later than the month in which a science fiction book was offered as a first choice.

	1ST CHOICE					2ND CHOICE				
	MYSTERY	ROMANCE	SCI. FICTION	THRILLER	WESTERN	JANUARY	FEBRUARY	MARCH	APRIL	MAY
JANUARY										
FEBRUARY										
MARCH										
APRIL										
MAY										
2ND CHOICE MYSTERY										
2ND CHOICE ROMANCE										
2ND CHOICE SCI. FICTION										
2ND CHOICE THRILLER										
2ND CHOICE WESTERN										

A new diet club was started in Phattsburg. The first five members to join up are named: Biggs, Gross, House, Piles, and Tubbs. Two of them are men named Barney and Whalen, while three of them are women named Bertha, Fanny, and Fatima. Each started out at a different one of these five weights: 300 lbs., 275 lbs., 250 lbs., 225 lbs., and 200 lbs. After three months on the diet, each person had lost a different amount of weight, either 125, 100, 75, 50, or 25 lbs. From the information given, determine each person's first and last name, original weight, and amount of weight lost.

1. At the beginning of the diet Whalen weighed less than Mr. Piles and the woman who lost the most weight in the whole group but more than Ms. House and the woman who lost the least weight of the whole group.

2. Barney did not lose exactly 75 lbs. and he is not now the same weight as Ms. Gross.

3. Mr. Tubbs, at the beginning of the diet, weighed more than Ms. Biggs and less than Fanny.

4. Fatima started out lighter but lost twice as much weight as Ms. Biggs.

	125 LBS.	100 LBS.	75 LBS.	50 LBS.	25 LBS.	BARNEY	BERTHA	FANNY	FATIMA	WHALEN	BIGGS	GROSS	HOUSE	PILES	TUBBS
300 LBS.															
275 LBS.															
250 LBS.															
225 LBS.															
200 LBS.															
BIGGS															
GROSS															
HOUSE															
PILES															
TUBBS															
BARNEY															
BERTHA															
FANNY															
FATIMA															
WHALEN															

Ms. Smith plans her week's work and pleasure precisely. She schedules a different activity each weekday for the morning, afternoon, and evening, in addition to her daily chores of making beds, doing dishes, etc. In the mornings she keeps one free, works at a hospital, does her ironing, does her laundry, and helps out at the nursery where her youngest child attends. The activities occupying her afternoons are: cleaning the bathrooms, gardening, cleaning the kitchen, cleaning the upstairs, and vacuuming. The five activities that occupy her evening are: bowling, bridge, class at the local H.S., gym class, and going to the movies. From the information given, determine what she does in the morning, afternoon, and evening of each day Monday through Friday.

1. The morning that she has free, except for daily chores, is on an earlier day of the week than the afternoon when she does the gardening but later than the afternoon when she does the vacuuming, which is not Monday.
2. Her gym class is not on Friday but it is later in the week than the night when she goes bowling, which in turn is later in the week than the night when she plays bridge, but none of these evening activities is on the same day when she has a free morning.
3. She does the laundry and cleans the bathroom on the same day.
4. She has already been to her night class before she has an afternoon to work in the garden but she has yet to put in her morning of volunteer work at the hospital.
5. She works at the nursery school later in the week than the day when she cleans the kitchen floor.

	MORNING					AFTERNOON					EVENING				
	FREE	HOSPITAL	IRONING	LAUNDRY	NURSERY	BATHROOMS	GARDENING	KITCHEN	UPSTAIRS	VACUUMING	BOWLING	BRIDGE	CLASS	GYM	MOVIES
MONDAY															
TUESDAY															
WEDNESDAY															
THURSDAY															
FRIDAY															
EVENING BOWLING															
EVENING BRIDGE															
EVENING CLASS															
EVENING GYM															
EVENING MOVIES															
AFTERNOON BATHROOMS															
AFTERNOON GARDENING															
AFTERNOON KITCHEN															
AFTERNOON UPSTAIRS															
AFTERNOON VACUUMING															

38. RETURNING FROM VACATION

Five couples who live on Maple Avenue in Forestville were all away on vacation for the same two weeks during the summer. The Smiths had kept the keys to the houses of all five couples in order to water the plants, etc. The couples are named: Finn, Gersten, Hawkins, O'Malley, and Webster. They were each on vacation in a different one of these five cities: Denver, Las Vegas, Los Angeles, Reno, and Vancouver. Each couple returned by a different means of transportation, either: airplane, boat, bus, car, or train. From the information given, determine the order in which they returned, where they had been, and how they got home.

1. The Websters arrived home earlier than the couple who were in Las Vegas but later than the couple who came back by airplane.
2. The couple returning from Reno did not come by boat but they arrived after the couple returning from L.A.
3. The Hawkins arrived home before the Gerstens but after the Finns, who didn't return by airplane.
4. The couple who returned by bus arrived home later than the couple who returned by train but before the Hawkinses, however, none of these three couples had been to Denver or Vancouver.
5. The first couple to arrive home had not been to L.A., Reno, or Vancouver, and neither had the Finns.

	FINN	GERSTEN	HAWKINS	O'MALLEY	WEBSTER	AIRPLANE	BOAT	BUS	CAR	TRAIN	DENVER	LAS VEGAS	LOS ANGELES	RENO	VANCOUVER
FIRST															
SECOND															
THIRD															
FOURTH															
FIFTH															
DENVER															
LAS VEGAS															
LOS ANGELES															
RENO															
VANCOUVER															
AIRPLANE															
BOAT															
BUS															
CAR															
TRAIN															

39. DOG HOUSE

Five women friends each live on a different floor of the North Star apartment building. Their names are: Edith, Hannah, Linda, Michelle, and Sarah. They each own a dog. Each dog is one of these types: cocker spaniel, dachshund, pekingese, poodle, and schnauzer. The dogs are named: Buttercup, Daisy, Pansy, Rose, and Violet. From the information given, determine the floor on which each woman lives as well as the name and type of dog owned by each one.

1. Linda lives on a higher floor than the dog named Buttercup but on a lower floor than the pekingese, which is not named Rose.
2. Edith and her dog live on a higher floor than the dog named Pansy but on a lower floor than the dog named Buttercup, however, none of these dogs is a schnauzer.
3. The dachshund lives on a higher floor than the poodle but a lower floor than Sarah, whose dog is not a pekingese.
4. Violet is not a schnauzer but lives on a lower floor than Michelle.

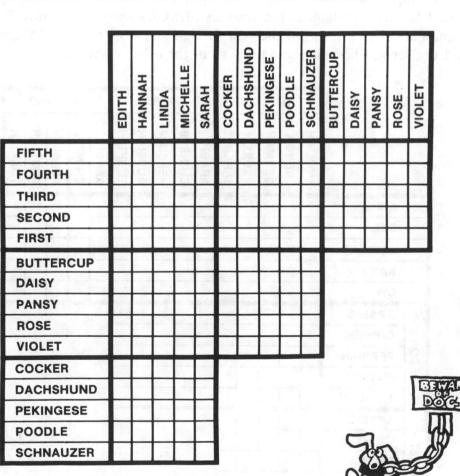

	EDITH	HANNAH	LINDA	MICHELLE	SARAH	COCKER	DACHSHUND	PEKINGESE	POODLE	SCHNAUZER	BUTTERCUP	DAISY	PANSY	ROSE	VIOLET
FIFTH															
FOURTH															
THIRD															
SECOND															
FIRST															
BUTTERCUP															
DAISY															
PANSY															
ROSE															
VIOLET															
COCKER															
DACHSHUND															
PEKINGESE															
POODLE															
SCHNAUZER															

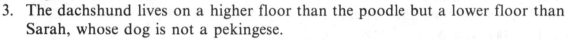

40. INTERPRETERS

There are five interpreters at the U.N. whose names are: Aix, Dee, Jay, Kay, and Oh. Each one is a native speaker of a different one of these five languages: English, French, German, Hebrew, and Japanese. They each speak two other languages fluently. The five best languages spoken are: Arabic, Chinese, Persian, Russian, and Turkish. As it happens the five second best languages of the five interpreters are these same languages. Aix and Dee are women while Jay, Kay, and Oh are men. From the information given, determine each person's native language and his first and second best foreign language.

1. The native English speaker doesn't speak Russian at all.
2. The Japanese and the German both list Russian as one of the languages that they speak but neither man is Mr. Jay who is not French.
3. Mr. Kay is not Japanese.
4. Ms. Dee's best foreign language is the same as Mr. Oh's second best foreign language.
5. Neither woman speaks Persian but the best foreign language of one of them is Chinese and the second best foreign language of the other is Arabic.

	NATIVE					FIRST					SECOND				
	ENGLISH	FRENCH	GERMAN	HEBREW	JAPANESE	ARABIC	CHINESE	PERSIAN	RUSSIAN	TURKISH	ARABIC	CHINESE	PERSIAN	RUSSIAN	TURKISH
AIX															
DEE															
JAY															
KAY															
OH															
SECOND ARABIC															
SECOND CHINESE															
SECOND PERSIAN															
SECOND RUSSIAN															
SECOND TURKISH															
FIRST ARABIC															
FIRST CHINESE															
FIRST PERSIAN															
FIRST RUSSIAN															
FIRST TURKISH															

41. AMATEUR HOUR

The five top finishers in an amateur contest at the local high school in Middletown are named: Carl, Derek, James, Milton, and Wendel. Their last names are: Cudahy, Donnelly, Jenkins, Marlow, and Wilkins. No contestant has a double-letter monogram. Their five acts were as a juggler, magician, mimic, singer, and violinist. From the information given, determine the order of finish in the contest for each type of performer as well as each one's first and last name.

1. The mimic finished better than James but not as well as Derek.
2. James is not the juggler.
3. Mr. Wilkins did better than Mr. Marlow but not as well as Mr. Cudahy who didn't do as well as the magician.
4. Milton's last name is not Wilkins or Donnelly.
5. The violinist did not finish as well as Mr. Marlow who didn't do as well as Mr. Donnelly.

	JUGGLER	MAGICIAN	MIMIC	SINGER	VIOLINIST	CARL	DEREK	JAMES	MILTON	WENDEL	CUDAHY	DONNELLY	JENKINS	MARLOW	WILKINS
FIRST															
SECOND															
THIRD															
FOURTH															
FIFTH															
CUDAHY															
DONNELLY															
JENKINS															
MARLOW															
WILKINS															
CARL															
DEREK															
JAMES															
MILTON															
WENDEL															

At the twenty-year class reunion of the class of 1962 of the Littleboro High School, the ex-president, ex-vice-president, ex-secretary, ex-treasurer, and ex-prom committee chairperson of the senior class all showed up. Their last names are: Carter, Conway, Matson, Rollings, and Wilson. Three of them are boys named: Bill, Glen, and Phil. Two of them are girls named Liz and Mary. At present they each hold a different one of these five jobs: banker, beautician, C.P.A., doctor, and teacher. From the information given, determine the first and last name of each class officer, the class position each one held, and each one's present job.

1. The ex-president and ex-treasurer are both males but it is the other male who works as a C.P.A.
2. Bill's last name does not begin with a "C" and Mary's last name is not Wilson.
3. Mr. Conway, Phil, and the guy who used to be the secretary do not work as either a banker or a beautician.
4. Liz and the banker are not named Matson or Carter and none of these four is the ex-president.
5. The ex-president, ex-vice-president, and the doctor are not named Wilson.

	BILL	GLEN	LIZ	MARY	PHIL	CARTER	CONWAY	MATSON	ROLLINGS	WILSON	BANKER	BEAUTICIAN	C.P.A.	DOCTOR	TEACHER
EX-PRESIDENT															
EX-VICE-PRES.															
EX-SECRETARY															
EX-TREASURER															
EX-PROM COMM.															
BANKER															
BEAUTICIAN															
C.P.A.															
DOCTOR															
TEACHER															
CARTER															
CONWAY															
MATSON															
ROLLINGS															
WILSON															

43. ROCK TOUR

The Woebegones are a European rock band touring the United States. Five of the cities at which they performed concerts are: Buffalo, Cleveland, Kansas City, Los Angeles, and New York City. In each of these cities the concert was opened by one of these five bands: Crazy Glues, Double Double, Draw Backward, Right Turn, and Street Crazed. The attendances at the five concerts were: 70,000, 60,000, 50,000, 30,000, and 25,000. From the information given, determine the order in which they played the five cities, the attendance, and the name of the opening band.

1. Cleveland was later in the tour than Buffalo but earlier than K.C. which was earlier than the city where they had the largest crowd.
2. Draw Backward was not the opening act for the largest crowd but they opened for a larger crowd than the Crazy Glues.
3. Street Crazed opened in a city that was later in the tour than N.Y.C. but earlier than Cleveland.
4. The crowd when Double Double was the opening act was larger than in Cleveland but exactly one half of the crowd at the N.Y.C. concert.

	BUFFALO	CLEVELAND	K.C.	L.A.	N.Y.C.	CRAZY GLUES	DOUBLE DOUBLE	DRAW BACKWARD	RIGHT TURN	STREET CRAZED	70,000	60,000	50,000	30,000	25,000
FIRST															
SECOND															
THIRD															
FOURTH															
FIFTH															
70,000															
60,000															
50,000															
30,000															
25,000															
CRAZY GLUES															
DOUBLE DOUBLE															
DRAW BACKWARD															
RIGHT TURN															
STREET CRAZED															

44. ARCADE PRIZES

Tony manages the dart-throwing booth in the arcade at the local amusement park. He keeps the prizes available for the rubes to win on a set of five shelves. On each shelf he keeps three different types of prizes. On the left-hand sides of the shelves he keeps: ashtrays, electronic games, toy trains, watches, and water pistols. On the right-hand sides of the shelves he keeps: blenders, stereos, stuffed animals, TVs, and whistles. On the centers of the shelves he keeps: candy, clocks, dolls, toy boats, and wallets. From the information given, determine which prizes he keeps on the center, the left-hand side, and the right-hand side of each of the five shelves.

1. Toy boats are on a lower shelf than the one that holds electronic games and TVs but on a higher shelf than the one that holds water pistols and blenders.
2. Dolls and TVs are not on the same shelf.
3. Wallets are on a higher shelf than candy but on a lower shelf than blenders, however, toy trains are not on the same shelf as any of these items.
4. Watches are on a higher shelf than whistles but on a lower shelf than the stereos.

		LEFT					RIGHT					CENTER				
		ASHTRAYS	GAMES	TOY TRAINS	WATCHES	PISTOLS	CANDY	CLOCKS	DOLLS	TOY BOATS	WALLETS	BLENDERS	STEREOS	ANIMALS	T.V.'S	WHISTLES
	FIFTH															
	FOURTH															
	THIRD															
	SECOND															
	FIRST															
RIGHT	BLENDERS															
	STEREOS															
	ANIMALS															
	T.V.'S															
	WHISTLES															
CENTER	CANDY															
	CLOCKS															
	DOLLS															
	TOY BOATS															
	WALLETS															

45. PICNIC TOYS

The five Johnson children each brought a toy to the family picnic on the Fourth of July. Their ages are: 16, 12, 10, 8, and 6. Their names are: Alice, Billy, Brenda, Greg, and Sally. A ball, a frisbee, a hoop, a kite, and a rope are the five toys that they brought, which are each a different one of these five colors: blue, gold, red, silver, and white. From the information given, determine each child's name and age as well as the color of the toy that each one brought.

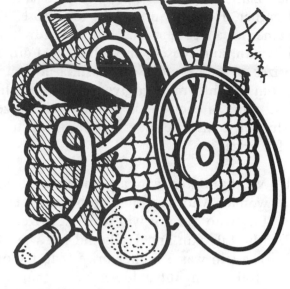

1. The 6-year-old and the 16-year-old children are the same sex and one brought something silver and the other brought the frisbee.
2. The rope and the kite are not blue or gold.
3. Alice is older than Billy but younger than the girl who brought the hoop.
4. The girl who brought the kite is older than Brenda who is older than the kid who brought the ball.
5. The kid who brought the red toy is older than the girl who brought the rope but younger than the girl who brought the blue toy.

	ALICE	BILLY	BRENDA	GREG	SALLY	BALL	FRISBEE	HOOP	KITE	ROPE	BLUE	GOLD	RED	SILVER	WHITE
16															
12															
10															
8															
6															
BLUE															
GOLD															
RED															
SILVER															
WHITE															
BALL															
FRISBEE															
HOOP															
KITE															
ROPE															

Five women won the top five prizes in a big
national sweepstakes contest. Their names are:
Heather, Holly, Laurel, Lily, and Rose. Their last
names are: Heatherton, Hollyer, Laurelton,
Lilyman, and Rosen. In alphabetical order, the five
prizes were: a boat, a car, cash, a house, and a trip.
From the information given, determine the first and
last name of each of the winners, the prize won, and
whether it was the first, second, third, fourth, or
fifth prize.

1. Ms. Laurelton won a higher prize than the
   woman who won the trip but a lower prize than
   Lily who did not win the first prize.
2. Ms. Lilyman and Holly did not win the car.
3. The trip was a higher prize than the one that
   Holly won but a lower prize than the one that
   Heather won which was not the first prize.
4. The cash was a higher prize than the car but a lower prize than the one that
   Laurel won.
5. Ms. Heatherton won a higher prize than Ms. Hollyer but a lower prize than the
   house.

	BOAT	CAR	CASH	HOUSE	TRIP	HEATHER	HOLLY	LAUREL	LILY	ROSE	HEATHERTON	HOLLYER	LAURELTON	LILYMAN	ROSEN
FIRST															
SECOND															
THIRD															
FOURTH															
FIFTH															
HEATHERTON															
HOLLYER															
LAURELTON															
LILYMAN															
ROSEN															
HEATHER															
HOLLY															
LAUREL															
LILY															
ROSE															

Three girls named Beverly, Julie, and Lucy, as well as two boys named Philip and Warren, each managed a stall at the school fair. The last names of the five children are: Brewster, Burger, Glover, Latham, and Standish. The five booths managed were: a book stall, a cake stall, a crafts stall, a funny fotos booth, and a penny toss game. The profits made at the booths were: $80.00, $65.00, $50.00, $40.00, and $25.00. From the information given, determine the first and last name of each child, the type of booth managed, and the amount of profit made.

1. Beverly and the girl who made the most money did not operate the funny fotos booth.
2. Lucy made less money than the cake booth but more than the penny toss booth.
3. Miss Burger made only half as much money as Philip but neither operated the cake or crafts booths.
4. Warren made more money than the Standish boy but neither operated the funny fotos or penny toss booths.
5. The kid operating the crafts booth made less money than Miss Glover but more than Miss Latham.

	BOOKS	CAKES	CRAFTS	FUNNY FOTOS	PENNY TOSS	BEVERLY	JULIE	LUCY	PHILIP	WARREN	BREWSTER	BURGER	GLOVER	LATHAM	STANDISH
$80.00															
$65.00															
$50.00															
$40.00															
$25.00															
BREWSTER															
BURGER															
GLOVER															
LATHAM															
STANDISH															
BEVERLY															
JULIE															
LUCY															
PHILIP															
WARREN															

48. BIRD HOUSES

Presently being boarded at the Bird House are five birds, which are: a canary, a cockatoo, a myna bird, a parakeet, and a parrot. The owners of these birds are named: Crane, Finch, Hawk, Heron, and Raven. In alphabetical order, the first names of the two men are: Jay and Martin, while the three women are Mavis, Polly, and Robin. They each live on a different one of these five streets: Birdsall Street, Downs Street, Fowler Avenue, Poltrecci Avenue, and Winger Street. From the information given, determine the first and last name of each pet's owner as well as the name of the street on which each one lives.

1. Polly does not own the parakeet or the parrot but one of these two birds belongs to Ms. Heron and the other one lives on Winger Street.
2. Martin is not Mr. Crane and neither of these two men lives on Birdsall Street or Fowler Avenue.
3. Robin, Ms. Heron, and the woman who lives on Downs Street do not own the myna bird or the parakeet.
4. Ms. Finch, Mr. Hawk, and the canary's owner do not live on Poltrecci Avenue or Birdsall Street.
5. The canary does not live on Fowler Avenue.

	BIRDSALL	DOWNS	FOWLER	POLTRECCI	WINGER	JAY	MARTIN	MAVIS	POLLY	ROBIN	CRANE	FINCH	HAWK	HERON	RAVEN
CANARY															
COCKATOO															
MYNA BIRD															
PARAKEET															
PARROT															
CRANE															
FINCH															
HAWK															
HERON															
RAVEN															
JAY															
MARTIN															
MAVIS															
POLLY															
ROBIN															

SOLUTIONS

1. PROM DRESSES

The girl who wore a blue dress is not Nora or Pamela (Clue 4) Margery or Ramona (Clue 1) so she is Gail, therefore her last name is Jensen (Clue 5). Pamela wore a green dress (Clue 5) and her last name is Oblinski (Clue 2). Ms. Smith wore an orange dress (Clue 2) and her first name is not Margery (Clue 3) or Nora (Clue 4) so it is Ramona. Margery did not wear a pink dress (Clue 3) so she wore a yellow dress and Nora wore a pink dress. Nora's last name is not Clausen (Clue 4) so it is Mathers and Margery's last name is Clausen.

In Summary:

Gail — Jensen — Blue
Margery — Clausen — Yellow
Nora — Mathers — Pink
Pamela — Oblinski — Green
Ramona — Smith — Orange

2. DOUBLE GIFTS

Vivian bought herself a necklace (Clue 2) and she bought her friend a watch (Clue 4); therefore, Rita bought herself a watch (Clue 4) but she didn't buy their friend a necklace (Clue 2), a sweater, or a wallet (Clue 1), so she bought her gloves. Nancy did not buy herself a sweater or a wallet (Clue 1) so she bought gloves, and for her friend she didn't buy a sweater or a wallet (Clue 1) so she bought her a necklace. Sally did not buy herself a sweater (Clue 5) so she bought a wallet, and Olivia bought a wallet for herself (Clue 3), which leaves a sweater to be the gift that Olivia bought for herself and Sally bought for their friend.

In Summary:

Friend — Self
Nancy — Necklace — Gloves
Olivia — Wallet — Sweater
Rita — Gloves — Watch
Sally — Sweater — Wallet
Vivian — Watch — Necklace

3. TEST CARS' MPG'S

The green car got better mpg than two cars (Clue 4) but less mpg than two cars (Clue 1), so it got 30 mpg. The red car got 32 mpg and the car driven by Durham got 31 mpg (Clue 1). The yellow car got 29 mpg and the car driven by Gosling got 28 mpg (Clue 4). Since Durham got 31 and Gosling got 28, Cox must have driven either the red car for 32 mpg, the green for 30 mpg, or the yellow for 29 mpg, but he didn't drive the red or green car (Clue 3), so he drove the yellow car. Wollinsky did not get the top mpg (Clue 2) so he drove the green car and got 30 mpg, which leaves Heynek to be the driver of the red car, which got 32 mpg. The blue car did not get the least mpg (Clue 2) so it was the one driven by Durham that got 31 mpg, and the white car was the one driven by Gosling that got 28 mpg.

In Summary:

32 mpg — Red — Heynek
31 mpg — Blue — Durham
30 mpg — Green — Wollinsky
29 mpg — Yellow — Cox
28 mpg — White — Gosling

4. BANK WORKERS

Buck's last name is not El Grande, Finn, or Nicholson (Clue 1) or Cash (Clue 4), so it is Coyne; since he is not the regular teller (Clue 4), he is the head teller (Clue 3). The regular teller's name is, therefore, Nicholson (Clue 3). Senta's last name is not Finn (Clue 2), Cash (Clue 4), or El Grande (Clue 5), so she is Ms. Nicholson. The president's last name is not Finn or El Grande (Clue 1), so it is Cash. Penny's last name is not El Grande (Clue 5) and, since she is not the president (Clue 1), it is not Cash, so it is Finn. Nick is not the president (Clue 5), so he is El Grande and Mr. Cash, the president, is named Bill. Penny Finn is not the security guard (Clue 2), so Nick El Grande is and Penny Finn is the bank officer.

In Summary:

Head Teller — Buck — Coyne
Officer — Penny — Finn
President — Bill — Cash
Security guard — Nick — El Grande
Teller — Senta — Nicholson

5. BASEBALL-HITTING CONTEST

The man who hit the ball the farthest is not Tom (Clue 1), Carl or Marty (Clue 2), or Fred (Clue 3), so it was Biff. His last name is not Miller (Clue 1), MacNab or Keech (Clue 3), or Winslow (Clue 4), so it is Jenkins. The man who hit the ball the shortest distance is not Carl (Clue 2), Fred (Clue 3), or Tom (Clue 4), so it is Marty. His last name is not Miller (Clue 1),

Keech (Clue 3), or Winslow (Clue 4), so it is MacNab. Tom's last name is not Miller (Clue 1) or Winslow (Clue 4), so it is Keech and he hit the ball farther than Mr. Winslow (Clue 4), but not as far as Mr. Miller (Clue 1)—so Miller hit one 300 feet, Tom Keech 275 feet, and Winslow 250 feet. Fred didn't hit the ball as far as Tom Keech (Clue 3) so he is Mr. Winslow, which leaves Carl to be Mr. Miller.

In Summary:

325 — Biff — Jenkins
300 — Carl — Miller
275 — Tom — Keech
250 — Fred — Winslow
200 — Marty — MacNab

6. CANDIDATES

Hargreaves and Jensen were not first- or fifth-place vote-getters (Clue 1) so Hargreaves came in second, the Liberal candidate third and Jensen fourth (Clue 4). Nelson did better than Liebowitz but not the best (Clue 2), so Nelson finished third as the Liberal candidate and Liebowitz finished fifth, which leaves Goshen to be the top vote-getter. The Republican finished better than Nelson (Clue 2) but not first (Clue 1), so he is Hargreaves. The first place candidate is either Democrat or Independent (Clue 1) but since his name is Goshen, he is not the Independent (Clue 3)—so he is the Democrat and the Independent candidate is Liebowitz, which leaves the Conservative to be Mr. Jensen, who came in fourth.

In Summary:

First — Democrat — Goshen
Second — Republican — Hargreaves
Third — Liberal — Nelson
Fourth — Conservative — Jensen
Fifth — Independent — Liebowitz

7. BIRTHDAYS IN JUNE

The girl who received a dress (Clue 1) is not Elvira or Joan (Clue 3), so it is Mary. Douglas did not receive the coat (Clue 1), the electronic game (Clue 2), or the book (Clue 4), so his present was concert tickets. Timothy did not receive the coat (Clue 1) or an electronic game (Clue 2), so his present was the book. Elvira did not receive an electronic game (Clue 2) so Joan did, and therefore Elvira's present was the coat. Elvira's birthday is preceded by two others (Clue 2) and since she received the coat, it is followed by two others (Clue 1), so she was born on the 12th. Joan, who received the electronic game, was born on June first and Douglas, who received the concert tickets, was born on the seventh (Clue 2). Timothy was born on June 20th and Mary on June 29th (Clue 1).

In Summary:

June 1 — Joan — Electronic Game
June 7 — Douglas — Concert Tickets
June 12 — Elvira — Coat
June 20 — Timothy — Book
June 29 — Mary — Dress

8. WIN, PLACE, AND SHOW PLUS TWO

The winning jockey was not Alvarez (Clue 1), Pickman, or Perez (Clue 2), or Wilson (Clue 4), so it was Hernandez and he must have ridden Quartermain (Clue 1), therefore, Alvarez rode Whirlaway. The fifth-place jockey was not Pickman (Clue 2) or Wilson (Clue 4) so it was Perez. Wilson did not ride Top Drawer or Nightshade (Clue 4), so he rode Full Sweep and didn't finish third (Clue 3), fourth, or fifth (Clue 4), so he finished second. Pickman finished fourth, Whirlaway with Alvarez up finished third, and Perez finished fifth (Clue 2). Top Drawer finished fourth (Clue 4) and was therefore Pickman's mount, and Perez rode Nightshade to a fifth-place finish.

In Summary:

First — Quartermain — Hernandez
Second — Full Sweep — Wilson
Third — Whirlaway — Alvarez
Fourth — Top Drawer — Pickman
Fifth — Nightshade — Perez

9. B-BALL PLAYERS

Oscar is taller than two other players (Clue 1) and shorter than two other players (Clue 4) so he is 6'3". Tony is 6' (Clue 1). The tallest is not Bill or Sammy (Clue 2) so it is Ernie. Bill is 6'5" and Sammy is 6'1" (Clue 2). 6'1" Sammy is nicknamed Tree (Clue 1). Slats is taller than Bill (Clue 2) so he is 6'6" Ernie. Stretch is taller than Oscar (Clue 4) so he is 6'5" Bill. Tony is not nicknamed Tiny (Clue 3), so Oscar is and 6' Tony is nicknamed Tower.

In Summary:

6'6" — Slats — Ernie
6'5" — Stretch — Bill
6'3" — Tiny — Oscar
6'1" — Tree — Sammy
6' — Tower— Tony

10. EYE DOCTORS

The man who wears bifocals is not Henry or Herbert (Clue 2), Harry or Horace (Clue 4) so it is Harlon, therefore, his last name is Eismann (Clue 3). Herbert wears tinted lenses (Clue 3) and his last name is Frayme (Clue 5). Mr. Glassman wears regular glasses (Clue 5) and his first name is not Harry (Clue 1) or Henry (Clue 2), so it is Horace. Harry does not wear reading glasses (Clue 1), so he wears contact lenses and Henry wears reading glasses. Henry's last name is not Lenz (Clue 2), so it is Rimbaud and Harry's last name is Lenz.

In Summary:

Harlon — Eismann — Bifocals
Harry — Lenz — Contact Lenses
Henry — Rimbaud — Reading glasses
Herbert — Frayme — Tinted glasses
Horace — Glassman — Regular glasses

11. WHERE ARE THE KIDS AT 11 P.M.?

The eldest is a daughter (Clue 1) but not Grace (Clue 3), so it is Cathy; she is not watching TV or sleeping (Clue 1), drawing (Clue 3) or reading (Clue 4), so she is doing a crossword puzzle. Grace is not drawing (Clue 3), reading or watching TV (Clue 2) so she is sleeping. The one who is reading is not Ryan or Albert (Clue 4) so it is Daniel. Since the child who is drawing is younger than Daniel the reader (Clue 3), and Ryan is older than he (Clue 4), the one who is drawing must be Albert, which leaves Ryan to be the one who is watching TV. Combining Clues 3 and 4 we see the boys from eldest to youngest are Ryan, Daniel, and Albert. Since Grace is younger still (Clue 3), she must be 14 and the three boys are: Ryan 17, Daniel 16, and Albert 15.

In Summary:

18 — Cathy — Crossword puzzles
17 — Ryan — Watching TV
16 — Daniel — Reading
15 — Albert — Drawing
14 — Grace — Sleeping

12. FORKS IN THE ROAD

The fourth fork leads to Houston and the fifth one leads to Tewsbury (Clue 1). Since Teasdale comes before the fork to Houston (Clue 1), then Stewartville is the first fork, Thousand Oaks the second fork, and Teasdale the third fork (Clue 4), which leaves Estwater to be the fork at the same place as Teasdale. The Thornberry fork is before the one to Houston but not first (Clue 1), so it is second. The Hornton fork does not also fork to Stewartville or Tewsbury (Clue 4), so it is with Houston. Stewartville is not at the same fork with Asterly (Clue 2), so it is with Seattle and Asterly is with Tewsbury.

In Summary:

First — Seattle — Stewartville
Second — Thornberry — Thousand Oaks
Third — Teasdale — Estwater
Fourth — Hornton — Houston
Fifth — Asterly — Tewsbury

13. WINTER VACATIONS

Their first and last vacations were not to Tahiti or Hawaii (Clue 1), since they are the two longest vacations, the five-day vacation was to Jamaica, Puerto Rico was their first and Bermuda was their last vacation (Clue 3). The Jamaican vacation was after January (Clue 4) so it was in February. Tahiti was not their longest vacation (Clue 4), so they went there for one week in December and they went for two weeks to Hawaii in January. They did not spend four days in Puerto Rico (Clue 2), so they spent three days there in November and four days in Bermuda in March.

In Summary:

November — Three days — Puerto Rico
December — One week — Tahiti
January — Two weeks — Hawaii
February — Five days — Jamaica
March — Four days — Bermuda

14. TOP LOCAL STATIONS

Two stations ranked lower than the muzak station (Clue 1) and two stations ranked higher (Clue 4), so it ranked third and WIGT ranked fifth. WTBG ranked second (Clue 4). WKCK ranked fourth and the jazz station ranked fifth (Clue 1). WTBG does not play rock or classical music (Clue 2), so it plays country music. WLTR did not rank fifth (Clue 3) so it ranked third and WIGT ranked fifth. Fourth-ranking WKCK plays classical music (Clue 3), which leave rock to be the type of music played on WWZZ.

In Summary:

First — WWZZ — Rock
Second — WTBG — Country
Third — WLTR — Muzak
Fourth — WKCK — Classical
Fifth — WIGT — Jazz

15. CB'ERS

The realtor is not called All 'Round Guy or Shifty (Clue 2), Big Daddy (Clue 3), or Lightning (Clue 5), so he is Hot Wheels. Pete is not Big Daddy (Clue 3), Hot Wheels (Clue 4), All 'Round Guy or Shifty (Clue 2), so he is Lightning. Al is not All 'Round Guy or Shifty (Clue 2), or Hot Wheels (Clue 4), so he is Big Daddy and he is not the trucker (Clue 4), salesman, or repairman (Clue 5), so he's the delivery man. Lightning Pete is not the salesman (Clue 1) or the trucker (Clue 4) so he is the repairman; therefore, Gus is the salesman and he is not Shifty (Clue 1), so he is All 'Round Guy. The trucker remains to be called Shifty; his name is not Ken (Clue 1), so it is Herb and Ken is Hot Wheels, the realtor.

In Summary:

All 'Round Guy — Gus — Salesman
Big Daddy — Al — Delivery man
Hot Wheels — Ken — Realtor
Lightning — Pete — Repairman
Shifty — Herb — Trucker

16. CAR POOL

The woman who drives a brown car (Clue 3) cannot be Ms. Browne (Clue 1), so it is Ms. Whyte. The person who drives on Friday is not Ms. Whyte, Mr. Greene, Mr. Grey (Clue 3), or Ms. Brown (Clue 4), so it is Mr. Tann; his car is not tan (Clue 1), green, or gray (Clue 2), so it is white. The person who drives on Monday is not Ms. Whyte with the brown car, Mr. Grey (Clue 3), or Ms. Browne (Clue 4), so it is Mr. Greene who does not drive a green car (Clue 1) or a tan car (Clue 2), so it is gray. Ms. Browne does not drive a tan car (Clue 4) so Mr. Grey does, and Ms. Browne's car is green; she drives earlier in the week than Mr. Grey in his tan car (Clue 4) but not on Tuesday (Clue 5), so she drives on Wednesday. Mr. Grey drives his tan car on Thursday (Clue 4) which leaves Ms. Whyte to be the one who drives on Tuesday.

In Summary:

Monday — Mr. Greene — Gray
Tuesday — Ms. Whyte — Brown
Wednesday — Ms. Browne — Greene
Thursday — Mr. Grey — Tan
Friday — Mr. Tann — White

17. BAY AREA MYSTERIES

The crime in San Jose was not arson or embezzlement (Clue 1), murder or kidnapping (Clue 3), so it was robbery. The crime in San Francisco was not arson or embezzlement (Clue 1) or kidnapping (Clue 4), so it was murder and its chief clue was not an eyewitness (Clue 1), tire track, phone tip (Clue 2), or a letter (Clue 3), so it was fingerprints. The robbery in San Jose was not solved by an eyewitness (Clue 1), a letter (Clue 3), or a tire track (Clue 4), so it was a phone tip that cracked the case. The crime of embezzlement was not solved by an eyewitness (Clue 1) or a tire track (Clue 2), so the clue was a letter. The kidnapping was not solved by a tire track (Clue 4), so it was solved by an eyewitness, leaving the crime of arson to be the one that was solved by a tire-track clue. The crime in Palo Alto was not kidnapping or

embezzlement (Clue 3), so it was arson. The crime in Berkeley was not embezzlement with the clue in a letter (Clue 5) so that the crime in Oakland, and the crime in Berkeley was the kidnapping which was solved by an eyewitness.

In Summary:

Berkeley — Kidnapping — Eyewitness
Oakland — Embezzlement — Letter
Palo Alto — Arson — Tire track
San Francisco — Murder — Fingerprints
San Jose — Robbery — Phone tip

18. COMMUTERS

The men are not the publisher or the secretary (Clue 1) or the receptionist (Clue 4), so they are the editor and the art director. Mr. Finch is not the editor (Clue 3) so he is the art director, and Mr. Marten is the editor. The three women do not come by railroad or car (Clue 2) so the two men do, but Mr. Finch does not come by railroad (Clue 3) so Mr. Marten does, and Mr. Finch comes by car. The publisher is not Hawk or Fulmer (Clue 2) so she is Ms. Gannett. The receptionist is not Fulmer (Clue 4) so the secretary is, and the receptionist is named Hawk; neither of these two walk to work (Clue 4) so Ms. Gannett does. The secretary does not take the bus (Clue 5) so the receptionist does, and the secretary rides the subway.

In Summary:

Mr. Finch — Car — Art Director
Mr. Marten — Railroad — Editor
Ms. Fulmer — Subway — Secretary
Ms. Gannet — Walk — Publisher
Ms. Hawk — Bus — Receptionist

19. POPULAR NEW SECRETARY

Her lunches on Thursday and Friday were not with Mr. Newman or Mr. Reynolds (Clue 1) or Mr. Price (Clue 2), so she had lunch with Mr. Farnsworth on Thursday and Mr. O'Malley on Friday (Clue 3). Those lunches were not Chinese or Greek (Clue 1) or French (Clue 3), so she had Mexican food on Thursday and Indian food on Friday (Clue 2). She did not have Chinese or Greek food with Mr. Price (Clue 1), so they had French food; it was not on Monday (Clue 3) or Wednesday (Clue 4) so it was on Tuesday. She had lunch with Mr. Newman on Wednesday (Clue 4), so she had lunch with Mr. Reynolds on Monday. Mr. Reynolds took her for Greek food and Mr. Newman took her for Chinese food (Clue 1).

In Summary:

Monday — Mr. Reynolds — Greek
Tuesday — Mr. Price — French
Wednesday — Mr. Newman — Chinese
Thursday — Mr. Farnsworth — Mexican
Friday — Mr. O'Malley — Indian

20. BOWLING TEAM AVERAGES

Mr. Sutain's average is higher than two others (Clue 2) and lower than two others (Clue 4), so it is 201. Mr. Dugon's average is 211 and Ivan's is 220 (Clue 4), so Ivan is Mr. Plotsky and Harmon has the lowest average (Clue 1). Harmon's last name is not Boyce (Clue 3) so it is Cardel, therefore, Mr. Boyce is the one with the 198 average and

his name is Jerry (Clue 2). Mr. Dugon is not named Willie (Clue 4), so he is Dennis and Willie must be Mr. Sutain.

In Summary:

220 — Ivan — Plotsky
211 — Dennis — Dugon
201 — Willie — Sutain
198 — Jerry — Boyce
195 — Harmon — Cardel

21. ANTIQUE SHOPPING

The cheapest item was not the chair (Clue 1), lamp (Clue 2), vase or desk (Clue 4), so it was the stool. The most expensive item was not the chair (Clue 1), lamp (Clue 3), or vase (Clue 4) so it was the desk. Ms. Comisky did not buy the desk, yet her item cost more than the lamp (Clue 3) which cost more than two other items (Clue 2), so Ms. Comisky bought something for $400.00. The lamp cost $300.00, Ms. Simmons spent $200.00 and Ms. Evans spent $100.00 for the stool (Clue 2). The chair cost $400.00, Ms. Addison's purchase cost $500.00 (the desk), and Ms. Wallis bought the lamp for $300.00 (Clue 1), which leaves the vase to be the $200.00 item purchased by Ms. Simmons.

In Summary:

$500.00 — Desk — Addison
$400.00 — Chair — Comisky
$300.00 — Lamp — Wallis
$200.00 — Vase — Simmons
$100.00 — Stool — Evans

22. SISTER CITIES

Monmouth is not the sister city of Appleboro (Clue 1) so it is the sister city of Keystown, and Appleboro is the sister city of a city in Canada (Clue 3). The sister city of Corley is not Appleboro, Bellville, or Peachburg (Clue 1), so it is Cherryvale, whose sister city is not in New Zealand (Clue 4), so Corley is in Australia and Monmouth is in New Zealand (Clue 1). Bellville's sister city is not in South Africa (Clue 4) so it is in Great Britain and the sister city of Peachburg is in South Africa. Poulson is not the sister city of Bellville, nor is it Peachburg's sister city in South Africa (Clue 4), so it is Appleboro's sister city in Canada. Newton is not in Great Britain (Clue 2) so it is in South Africa and Abbemount is Bellville's sister city in Great Britain.

In Summary:

Appleboro — Poulson — Canada
Bellville — Abbemount — Great Britain
Cherryvale — Corley — Australia
Keystown — Monmouth — New Zealand
Peachburg — Newton — South Africa

23. WHERE ARE THEY NOW?

There are three women and two men, so the lawyer must be a woman but not Ms. Black (Clue 3) or Ms. Brown (Clue 2), so she is Ms. Green. She lives in the U.S. but not in L.A. (Clue 3), so she lives in Philadelphia. A man lives in L.A. but not Mr. White (Clue 3) so it is Mr. Silver; he is not an artist (Clue 1), a diplomat (Clue 2), or a banker (Clue 4) so he is a florist. Ms. Black does not live in Cairo (Clue 1) or Paris (Clue 3) so she lives in Zurich; she is not an artist (Clue 1) or a diplomat (Clue 2) so she is a banker. Mr. White does not live in Paris (Clue 3) so Ms. Brown does and Mr. White lives in Cairo and he is not the artist (Clue 1) so he is the diplomat and Ms. Brown is the artist.

In Summary:

Mr. Silver — Florist — Los Angeles
Mr. White — Diplomat — Cairo
Ms. Black — Banker — Zurich
Ms. Brown — Artist — Paris
Ms. Green — Lawyer — Philadelphia

24. VIDEO WIZARD

His highest scoring game was not on Robot Blaster or Pool Shark (Clue 2) so it was on Mazerama (Clue 4). His lowest scoring game was not on Robot Blaster or Space Wars (Clue 2) or Pool Shark (Clue 4) so it was on Hot Rod Racer. On Space Wars, Robot Blaster, and Pool Shark he scored 200,000, 150,000, and 100,000, respectively (Clue 2). Neither his first nor his last game was on Mazerama, Hot Rod Racer, or Space Wars (Clue 1). Hi played Robot Blaster before Pool Shark (Clue 5) so he played Robot Blaster first and Pool Shark fifth. His second game, his third game, and his fourth game, respectively were Mazerama, Hot Rod Racer, and Space Wars (Clue 3).

In Summary:

First — Robot Blaster — 150,000
Second — Mazerama — 250,000
Third — Hot Rod Racer — 50,000
Fourth — Space Wars — 200,000
Fifth — Pool Shark — 100,000

25. DIVORCE

Ten years was the longest marriage (Clue 2). The man whose marriage lasted the longest is not Justin or Jeremy (Clue 1), Joseph (Clue 3), or James (Clue 4) so it is John. The woman who was divorced first is not Luanne or Rosette (Clue 1), Loreen (Clue 3), or Maybelle (Clue 4) so it is Bertrice. Returning to John, his wife was not Rosette (Clue 1), Loreen (Clue 3), or Maybelle (Clue 4) so it was Luanne. We can now determine some other number of years married; Justin was married for five years, Jeremy four years, and Rosette eight years (Clue 1). Loreen was married one year less than Justin (Clue 3) so she was married for four years to Jeremy and Joseph was married for three years to Bertrice (Clue 3), which leaves James to be the man who was married to Rosette for eight years. Loreen was not married to Justin (Clue 3) so Maybelle was and Loreen was married to Jeremy for four years.

In Summary:

10 — John — Luanne
8 — James — Rosette
5 — Justin — Maybelle
4 — Jeremy — Loreen
3 — Joseph — Bertrice

26. LITTLE LEAGUE TEAMS

The sponsor of the team that finished first is not City Bank (Clue 1), Decker Insurance Company (Clue 3), Mom's Bakery or Joe's Florist (Clue 4) so it is Al's Hardware. The team that finished fifth is not called the Panthers (Clue 1), Lions or Cougars (Clue 3), or Tigers (Clue 4) so they are the Bobcats. Since the team sponsored by Al's Hardware is not the Lions (Clue 2), then the Lions finished second, Decker Insurance finished third, and the Cougars finished fourth (Clue 3). The Tigers did not finish first (Clue 4) so the Panthers did and the Tigers finished third. The team sponsored by Joe's Florist is the Lions who finished second (Clue 4). The Bobcats are not the team sponsored by Mom's Bakery (Clue 2) so City Bank sponsors them and the Cougars are the team sponsored by Mom's Bakery.

In Summary:

First — Panthers — Al's Hardware
Second — Lions — Joe's Florist
Third — Tigers — Decker Insurance Co.
Fourth — Cougars — Mom's Bakery
Fifth — Bobcats — City Bank

27. CHOICE OF SHOWS

The comic at the Gold Rush is a woman (Clue 1); it is not Tomlin (Clue 2) and since both performers at the Gold Rush are women the comic is not Radner (Clue 4) so it is Rivers. The comic at the Gold Horn is a man (Clue 1), but not Brenner (Clue 2) so it is Carlin. The male comic appearing with Newton is not Brenner (Clue 3) so Newton is at the Gold Horn with Carlin. The comic at the Gold Dust is not Brenner or Tomlin (Clue 2) so it is Radner. Channing is appearing at either the Gold Dust or the Gold Rush (Clue 2) but not at the Gold Dust with Radner (Clue 4) so Channing is with Rivers at the Gold Rush. The male Singer with Radner is not Williams (Clue 4) so it is Jones. Williams is not at the Silver Bell (Clue 4) so Minnelli is, and Williams is at the Silver Dollar where the comic is not a male (Clue 1) so it is Tomlin. Brenner is with Minnelli at the Silver Bell.

In Summary:

Gold Dust — Tom Jones — Gilda Radner
Gold Horn — Wayne Newton — George Carlin
Gold Rush — Carol Channing — Joan Rivers
Silver Bell — Liza Minnelli — David Brenner
Silver Dollar — Andy Williams — Lily Tomlin

28. LUCKY CHARMS

Bluet is an infielder (Clue 2) and he doesn't play first or third base (Clue 4) so he is the shortstop. The penny is not the lucky charm of Browning (Clue 1), Greenfield, Whitehall, or Blacket (Clue 3) so it is Bluet's lucky charm. Greenfield is an outfielder (Clue 3) and the other outfielder is not Browning (Clue 1) or Whitehall (Clue 3) so it is Blacket. Blacket's lucky charm is not a silver dollar (Clue 1), clover (Clue 3), or a ribbon (Clue 4) so it is a rabbit's foot. Since Whitehall doesn't play first base (Clue 3), Browning must, and Whitehall plays third base. The rabbit's foot is not the lucky charm of the centerfielder (Clue 5), so it is the rightfielder's Blacket's, lucky charm. The centerfielder, therefore, is Greenfield. The ribbon is not the lucky charm of the first or third baseman (Clue 4) so this is Greenfield's lucky charm.

Browning the first baseman's lucky charm is not a silver dollar (Clue 1) so it is a clover and the silver dollar is the lucky charm of Whitehall the third baseman.

In Summary:

Blacket — Rabbit's foot — Rightfielder
Bluet — Penny — Shortstop
Browning — Clover — First baseman
Greenfield — Ribbon — Centerfielder
Whitehall — Silver dollar — Third baseman

29. WEARING OF THE GREEN

Mr. Flanagan is not Francis or Frank (intro.), Brian (Clue 2), or Mike (Clue 4) so he is Liam; and the green article of clothing he wore was not a hat or a scarf (Clue 2), a shirt or a tie (Clue 3) so it was a green pair of trousers. Mike's last name is not Maguire or Murphy (intro.) or Brady (Clue 3) so it is Lynch; and his green article of clothing was not a shirt or a tie (Clue 3) or a scarf (Clue 4) so it was a green hat. Mr. Maguire is not Francis (Clue 1) or Brian (Clue 2) so he is Frank; and he didn't wear a green shirt (Clue 1) or a green scarf (Clue 2) so he wore a green tie. Brian is not Mr. Brady (intro.) so he is Mr. Murphy and Francis is Mr. Brady who did not wear a green shirt (Clue 3) so Brian Murphy did and Francis Brady wore a green scarf.

In Summary:

Brian — Murphy — Shirt
Francis — Brady — Scarf
Frank — Maguire — Tie
Liam — Flanagan — Trousers
Mike — Lynch — Hat

30. RUBIK'S CUBE CONTEST

The girl who won is not Gretchen or Lily (Clue 1) she is Wendy and the color she begins with on top is not orange or green (Clue 1), red or blue (Clue 2), or yellow (Clue 3) so it is white. The girl who starts with red finished ahead of the girl who starts with blue (Clue 2) so Gretchen starts with red and Lily starts with blue (Clue 1). Eric does not start with orange or green (Clue 1) so he starts with yellow. Oswald finished after Lily (Clue 4) so he is not the one who starts with orange (Clue 2), therefore he starts with green on top and Wilbur starts with orange. Eric finished before Gretchen and Lily (Clue 1), so did Wilbur (Clue 2), and Oswald finished after Gretchen and Lily (Clue 4) so, Gretchen finished fourth, Lily fifth, and Oswald sixth. Eric, starting with yellow, finished second and Wilbur, starting with orange, finished third (Clue 3).

In Summary:

0:29 — Wendy — White
0:35 — Eric — Yellow
0:51 — Wilbur — Orange
1:10 — Gretchen — Red
1:26 — Lily — Blue
1:30 — Oswald — Green

31. LONG TRIP

The only person who was in the front seat for both halves of the trip was not Sanford or Oscar (Clue 2) or Jacob or Neil (Clue 3) so it was Bruce. He couldn't be the driver for the second half of the trip (Clue 4) so he drove for the first half and sat in the front passenger seat for the second half of the trip. The person who drove for the second half of the trip must be Oscar (Clue 2) and he was in the back center for the first half of the trip (Clue 4). In order for Clue 3 to work there must be two positions unused so far in the first and second half of the trip; these are the right rear and the left rear seats. Neil was not in the right rear seat for the first half of the trip (Clue 4) so Jacob was and Neil was in the left rear seat for the first half of the trip. Neil and Jacob switched places for the second half of the trip (Clue 3). This leaves Sanford to be the rider who sat in the front passenger seat for the first half of the trip and in the center rear seat for the second half of the trip.

In Summary:

	1st Half — 2nd Half
Bruce —	Driver — Front Passenger
Jacob —	Right rear — Left rear
Neil —	Left rear — Right rear
Oscar —	Center rear — Driver
Sanford —	Front passenger — Center rear

32. COUNTRY FAIR

Carl's favorite ride is not the dodgems (Clue 2), the round-up (Clue 3), ferris wheel or scrambler (Clue 4) so it is the whip, therefore Clark's favorite contest is the baseball throw (Clue 1) and Clark's favorite ride is not the dodgems (Clue 2), ferris wheel, or scrambler (Clue 4) so it is the round-up. Carl's favorite contest is not ring toss (Clue 2), darts or the horse race (Clue 3) so it is the sledge hammer. Carol's favorite contest is the horse race and her favorite ride is the dodgems (Clue 4). Clara does not like ring toss best (Clue 2) so she likes darts and Clare likes ring toss best. Clare's favorite ride is not the ferris wheel (Clue 5) so that is Clara's favorite ride and Clare likes the scrambler best.

In Summary:

Carl — Sledge Hammer — Whip
Carol — Horse Race — Dodgems
Clara — Darts — Ferris Wheel
Clare — Ring Toss — Scrambler
Clark — Baseball Throw — Round-up

33. WAKE-UP CALLS

A woman wishes to be called at 7:00 but it is not Ms. Farrell (Clue 2) or Ms. Brewster (Clue 3) so it is Ms. Desmond and her room number is not 945 or 900 (Clue 1), 915 or 930 (Clue 2) so it is 920. A woman has the highest room number (Clue 1) but it is not Ms. Brewster (Clue 3) so it is Ms. Farrell. Ms. Brewster's room number is lower than 920 (Clue 3) but not 900 (Clue 1) so it is 915. Mr. Donahue's room number is lower than Ms. Brewster's (Clue 4) so he is in room 900 and Mr. Hendricks is in room 930. The person who wishes to be called at 7:45 is not Mr. Donahue in room 900 (Clue 1), Brewster in 915, or Farrell in 945 (Clue 2) so it is Mr. Hendricks in room 930 who wishes to be called at 7:45. Ms. Brewster wishes to be called later than Ms. Farrell (Clue 2) but earlier than Mr. Donahue (Clue 4) so, Ms. Farrell in 945 wishes to be called at 7:15, Brewster in 915 at 7:20, and Donahue in 900 at 7:30.

In Summary:

7:00 — Ms. Desmond — 920
7:15 — Ms. Farrell — 945
7:20 — Ms. Brewster — 915
7:30 — Mr. Donahue — 900
7:45 — Mr. Hendricks — 930

34. FISH-RAISING KIDS

A boy has the smallest tank (Clue 1). He is not Martin (Clue 1) or Arthur (Clue 3) so Maurice has the smallest tank. A girl has the largest tank but it is not Alice (Clue 1) so it is Maureen. The neon tetras are not raised by Maureen or Maurice (Clue 1), Martin or Alice (Clue 1), so Arthur raises neon tetras and his tank is larger than at least 2 other tanks (Clue 3) and smaller than 2 other tanks (Clue 4) so Arthur's neon tetras are raised in a 25 gallon tank. Martin must have the 30 gallon tank (Clue 4) and that leaves Alice to be the one with the 20 gallon tank. Cichlids are raised by Maureen in the 50 gallon tank (Clue 4) and angelfish are raised by Alice in the 20 gallon tank (Clue 3). Maurice does not raise gouramis (Clue 2) so Martin does and Maurice raises guppies in his 10 gallon tank.

In Summary:

50 gal. — Maureen — Cichlids
30 gal. — Martin — Gouramis
25 gal. — Arthur — Neon tetras
20 gal. — Alice — Angelfish
10 gal. — Maurice — Guppies

35. BOOK OF THE MONTH CLUB

Westerns and mysteries were not offered in January or May (Clue 2) so a western was offered as the first choice in February, a mystery as the second choice in March, and a mystery as the first choice in April (Clue 3). A western was not offered as a second choice in February (Clue 1), January or May (Clue 2) so it was offered as the second choice in April. A romance novel was not offered as the second choice in January or May (Clue 4) so it was offered in February and a science fiction novel was offered as the second choice in January (Clue 4). This leaves a thriller to be the second choice in May. A romance novel was offered as the first choice later than February (Clue 4) so that is either March or May but if it was the one offered in March that would leave a thriller and a science fiction novel to be the first choices in January and May which the two parts of Clue 1 rule out since the second choices in those two months are already a thriller and a science fiction novel, therefore the romance novel was offered as a first choice in May. A science fiction novel could not be the first choice in January since a science fiction novel is the second choice (Clue 1) so it is the first choice offered in March and a thriller is the first choice offered in January.

In Summary:

        1st Choice — 2nd Choice
January — Thriller — Science Fiction
February — Western — Romance
March — Science Fiction — Mystery
April — Mystery — Western
May — Romance — Thriller

36. DIETERS' CLUB

Whalen started out at 250 lbs. (Clue 1). He is not Mr. Piles (Clue 1) so he is Mr. Tubbs and Barney is Mr. Piles. Ms. Biggs is not named Fanny (Clue 3) or Fatima (Clue 4) so she is Bertha. Ms. House weighs less than Whalen Tubbs (Clue 1) and Fanny weighed more (Clue 3) so Ms. House is Fatima and Ms. Gross is Fanny. These two women, Bertha Biggs and Fatima House, weighed less than 250, Whalen's weight, so Fatima began the diet at 200 lbs. and Bertha at 225 lbs. One of these two women is the one who lost the least on the diet (Clue 1) so it must be that Bertha Biggs lost 25 lbs. and Fatima House lost 50 lbs., twice as much (Clue 4). Fanny Gross lost the most weight, 125 lbs. (Clue 1). Barney Piles did not lose exactly 75 lbs. (Clue 2) so he lost 100 lbs. and Whalen Tubbs lost 75 lbs. If Barney Piles began the diet at 275 lbs. and lost 100 lbs., and if Fanny Gross started at 300 lbs. and lost 125 lbs. they would now be the same weight, but they are not (Clue 2) so Barney Piles started at 300 lbs. and Fanny Gross started at 275 lbs.

In Summary:

300 lbs. — 100 lbs. — Barney — Piles
275 lbs. — 125 lbs. — Fanny — Gross
250 lbs. — 75 lbs. — Whalen — Tubbs
225 lbs. — 25 lbs. — Bertha — Biggs
200 lbs. — 50 lbs. — Fatima — House

37. WORKDAYS

She doesn't work in the garden on Monday, Tuesday, or Wednesday (Clue 1), or Friday (Clue 4) she works in the garden on Thursday afternoon. She vacuums on Tuesday afternoon (Clue 1). She works at the hospital on Friday morning (Clue 4) and the free morning is Wednesday (Clue 1). The only day when we have not already determined what she does in either the morning or the afternoon is Monday so that must be when she does the laundry in the morning and cleans the bathrooms in the afternoon. She doesn't clean the kitchen on Friday afternoon (Clue 5) so she does it on Wednesday and she cleans the upstairs rooms on Friday afternoon. She works at the nursery school on Thursday morning (Clue 5) and does the ironing on Tuesday morning. Since her free morning is Wednesday, she plays bridge on Monday night, bowls on Tuesday, and goes to the gym on Thursday (Clue 2). Her evening class comes earlier in the week than the afternoon on which she gardens (Clue 4) so it is on Wednesday night and she goes to the movies on Friday night.

In Summary:

Monday — Laundry — Bathrooms — Bridge
Tuesday — Ironing — Vacuuming — Bowling
Wednesday — Free — Kitchen — Class
Thursday — Nursery — Gardening — Gym
Friday — Hospital — Upstairs — Movies

38. RETURNING FROM VACATION

The first couple to arrive home had not been to Las Vegas (Clue 1), L.A., Reno, or Vancouver (Clue 5) so they were returning from Denver. The Hawkinses did not return home last (Clue 3) so they arrived home fourth, the couple returning by bus arrived third, and the couple returning by train arrived second (Clue 4) because none of them were in Denver. The couple returning by airplane were not the fourth or fifth to arrive home (Clue 1) so they arrived home first. The Finns were not in L.A., Reno, or Vancouver (Clue 5) so they were in Las Vegas: two couples arrived home before them (Clue 1) and two after them (Clue 3) so they arrived home third. The Gerstens were the last to get home (Clue 3) and the Websters were second (Clue 1) so the O'Malleys were the first home. The second, third, and fourth couples to arrive home had not been in Vancouver (Clue 4) so the Gerstens were there. The couple returning from Reno arrived home fourth and the couple from L.A. second (Clue 2). The couple coming home from Reno did not come by boat (Clue 2) so they came by car and the Gerstens returned by boat from Vancouver.

In Summary:

First — O'Malley — Airplane — Denver
Second — Webster — Train — Los Angeles
Third — Finn — Bus — Las Vegas
Fourth — Hawkins — Car — Reno
Fifth — Gersten — Boat — Vancouver

39. DOG HOUSE

The dog named Buttercup does not live on either of the top two floors (Clue 1) or either of the bottom two floors (Clue 2) so Buttercup lives on the third floor. Linda lives on the fourth floor and the Pekingese on the top floor (Clue 1). Edith lives on the second floor (Clue 2). Since Sarah does not own a Pekingese, she doesn't live on the top floor (Clue 3) so she lives on the third floor. Michelle does not live on the bottom floor (Clue 4) so Hannah does, and Michelle lives on the top floor with her Pekingese whose name is not Rose (Clue 1), Pansy (Clue 2), or Violet (Clue 4), so it is Daisy. The dog named Pansy lives on the bottom floor below Edith (Clue 2). Since the schnauzer is not owned by Edith and is not called Buttercup or Pansy (Clue 2), it doesn't live on any of the bottom three floors so it lives on the fourth floor. Violet is not a schnauzer (Clue 4) so Rose is, and Violet is Edith's dog who lives on the second floor. Since Sarah lives on the third floor, her dog named Buttercup must be a cocker spaniel and the dachshund must live on the second floor, while the poodle must be Hannah's dog, Pansy, who lives on the bottom floor (Clue 3).

In Summary:

Fifth — Michelle — Pekingese — Daisy
Fourth — Linda — Schnauzer — Rose
Third — Sarah — Cocker spaniel — Buttercup
Second — Edith — Dachshund — Violet
First — Hannah — Poodle — Pansy

40. INTERPRETERS

The second best foreign language of the woman whose best foreign language is Chinese, is not Persian or Arabic (Clue 5) or Russian (Clue 2) so it is Turkish. The best foreign language of the woman whose second best foreign language is Arabic is not Persian (Clue 5) or Russian (Clue 2) so it is Turkish, therefore she is not Ms. Dee (Clue 4) so she is Ms. Aix and Ms. Dee is the woman who speaks Chinese and Turkish. Mr. Oh's second best foreign language is Chinese (Clue 4) and he must be either Japanese or German (Clue 2) so his best foreign language is Russian (Clue 2). Mr. Kay is either Japanese or German (Clue 2) but he is not Japanese (Clue 3) so he is German and Mr. Oh is Japanese. Mr. Kay, the German, has as his second best foreign language Russian (Clue 2) which leaves Persian to be the second best foreign language of Mr. Jay, which means Arabic must be Mr. Jay's best foreign language and Persian, Mr. Kay the German's, best foreign language. Since Mr. Jay and Ms. Aix speak Arabic, the English-speaking native is Ms. Dee (Clue 1). Mr. Jay is not French (Clue 2) so his native language is Hebrew and Ms. Aix is French.

In Summary:

Ms. Aix — French — Turkish — Arabic
Ms. Dee — English — Chinese — Turkish
Mr. Jay — Hebrew — Arabic — Persian
Mr. Kay — German — Persian — Russian
Mr. Oh — Japanese — Russian — Chinese

41. AMATEUR HOUR

Three people did better than Mr. Marlow (Clue 3) and he didn't finish fifth (Clue 5) so he finished fourth. Mr. Wilkins finished third and Mr. Cudahy finished second (Clue 3). Mr. Donnelly did not finish fifth (Clue 5) so he finished first and Mr. Jenkins finished fifth with an act as a violinist (Clue 5) and Mr. Donnelly's first place act was as a magician (Clue 3). Since Derek's last name cannot be Donnelly and James's last name cannot be Jenkins (intro.), Derek's last name is Cudahy who finished second, the mimic is Mr. Wilkins who finished third and James is James Marlow who finished fourth (Clue 1). James is not the juggler (Clue 2) so Derek Cudahy is and James Marlow is the singer. Milton's last name is not Wilkins or Donnelly (Clue 4) so it is Jenkins. Mr. Wilkins is not Wendel (intro.) so he is Carl and Mr. Donnelly is Wendel.

In Summary:

First — Magician — Wendel — Donnelly
Second — Juggler — Derek — Cudahy
Third — Mimic — Carl — Wilkins
Fourth — Singer — James — Marlow
Fifth — Violinist — Milton — Jenkins

42. CLASS REUNION

The ex-president and ex-treasurer are men (Clue 1) and so is the ex-secretary (Clue 3) so the ex-secretary is now a C.P.A. (Clue 1). The 2 women are the banker and the beautician (Clue 3). Therefore the ex-president and the ex-treasurer are a teacher and a doctor but the ex-president is not a doctor (Clue 5) so he is a teacher and the ex-treasurer is now a doctor. The 3 men are named Conway (Clue 3), Matson, and Carter (Clue 4). Bill's last name is not Conway or Carter (Clue 2) so he is Bill Matson and he is the third man who is the ex-secretary in Clue 3. Phil's last name is not Conway (Clue 3) so it is Carter and Mr. Conway is named Glen. Phil Carter is not the ex-president (Clue 4) so Glen Conway is and Phil Carter is the ex-treasurer. Liz is not the banker (Clue 4) so Mary is and Liz is the beautician. Mary the banker's last name is not Wilson (Clue 2) so it is Mary Rollings. Liz the beautician is named Wilson and she is not the ex-vice president (Clue 5) so she was prom committee chairperson and the ex-vice president is Mary Rollings, the banker.

In Summary:

Ex-President — Glen — Conway — Teacher
Ex-Vice-President — Mary — Rollings — Banker
Ex-Secretary — Bill — Matson — C.P.A.
Ex-Treasurer — Phil — Carter — Doctor
Ex-Prom Com — Liz — Wilson — Beautician

43. ROCK TOUR

Cleveland was not the fourth or fifth stop on the tour (Clue 1) nor the first or second (Clue 3) so it was the third stop. Buffalo was the second stop and K.C. the fourth stop (Clue 1). N.Y.C. was the first stop (Clue 3) which leaves L.A. as the fifth stop on the tour where they had a crowd of 70,000 (Clue 1). Street Crazed opened in Buffalo (Clue 3). The crowd at the concert opened by Double Double was either 25,000 or 30,000 to be half of N.Y.C.'s either 50,000 or 60,000 (Clue 4) but it was not the smallest crowd (Clue 4), which leaves 50,000 to be the size of the crowd that saw Street Crazed open for the show in Buffalo. Double Double with a crowd of 30,000 did not open in L.A. (since L.A. had the largest crowd) so they were the opening act in K.C. Draw Backward did not open for the largest or smallest crowd (Clue 2) so they opened for 60,000 in N.Y.C. The Crazy Glues opened for a smaller crowd (Clue 2) so they opened in Cleveland for a crowd of 25,000, leaving the group Right Turn to be the opening act in L.A.

In Summary:

1 — N.Y.C. — Draw Backward — 60,000
2 — Buffalo — Street Crazed — 50,000
3 — Cleveland — Crazy Glues — 25,000
4 — K.C. — Double Double — 30,000
5 — L.A. — Right Turn — 70,000

44. ARCADE PRIZES

There are two shelves above the one holding blenders (Clue 1) and there are two shelves below it (Clue 3) so blenders are on the third shelf. Wallets are on the second shelf and candy is on the bottom shelf (Clue 3). Toy boats are on the fourth shelf and T.V.s are on the top shelf (Clue 1). Dolls are not on the top shelf with the T.V.s (Clue 2) so they are on the third shelf and clocks must be on the top shelf. Electronic games are on the top shelf and water pistols are on the third shelf (Clue 1). Toy trains are not on shelves one or two with wallets or candy (Clue 3) so they are on the fourth shelf. Watches are not on the bottom shelf (Clue 4) so they are on the second shelf and ashtrays are on the bottom shelf. Since watches are on the second shelf, whistles are on the bottom shelf and stereos are on the fourth shelf (Clue 4) which leaves stuffed animals to be on the second shelf.

In Summary:

Left — Center — Right
Fifth —
    Electronic games — Clocks — TVs
Fourth —
    Toy trains — Toy boats — Stereos
Third —
    Water pistols — Dolls — Blenders
Second —
    Watches — Wallets — Stuffed animals
First —
    Ashtrays — Candy — Whistles

45. PICNIC TOYS

Alice is not the oldest or the youngest (Clue 3) and neither is Brenda (Clue 4) so the two boys must be 6 and 16 (Clue 1). Billy is not 16 (Clue 3) so he is 6 and Greg is 16. 16-year-old Greg did not bring the hoop (Clue 3), the kite, the ball (Clue 4), or the rope (Clue 5) so he brought the frisbee. The toy that Billy brought is silver (Clue 1): It was not a hoop (Clue 3), kite (Clue 4) or a rope (Clue 5) so it was a silver ball. The 12-year-old brought the rope (Clue 5). The rope is not gold (Clue 2) so it is white and Greg's frisbee must be gold. The kite is not blue (Clue 2) so the hoop is, and the kite is red. Brenda is the 8-year-old kid who brought the white rope (Clue 4). Alice is the 10-year-old kid who brought the red kite (Clue 3), which leaves Sally to be the 12-year-old kid who brought the blue hoop.

In Summary:

16 — Greg — Frisbee — Gold
12 — Sally — Hoop — Blue
10 — Alice — Kite — Red
8 — Brenda — Rope — White
6 — Billy — Ball — Silver

46. SWEEPSTAKES

The trip was either the fourth or fifth prize (Clue 1) but it was not the fifth prize (Clue 3) so it was the fourth prize. Lily won the second prize (Clue 1). Holly won the fifth prize (Clue 3); she did not win the cash (Clue 4), the car (Clue 2), or the house (Clue 5) so she won the boat. The cash was the second prize and the car was the third (Clue 4) which leaves the house to be the first prize and Laurel won it (Clue 4). Heather did not win the trip (Clue 3), so Rose did, and Heather won the car; her last name is Laurelton (Clue 1). Holly's last name is not Hollyer (intro.), Lilyman (Clue 2), or Heatherton (Clue 5) so it is Rosen. Ms. Heatherton won the second prize (Clue 5) so she is Lily the cash-winner. Ms. Hollyer is Rose the trip-winner (Clue 5); which leaves Ms. Lilyman to be Laurel the first prize winner who won the house.

In Summary:

First — House — Laurel — Lilyman
Second — Cash — Lily — Heatherton
Third — Car — Heather — Laurelton
Fourth — Trip — Rose — Hollyer
Fifth — Boat — Holly — Rosen

47. SCHOOL FAIR

Philip made twice as much money as Miss Burger (Clue 3) so he made either 50 or 80 dollars but he did not make 80 dollars, the most (Clue 1) so he made 50 dollars. The Standish boy is not Warren (Clue 4) so it is Philip Standish. Philip Standish's booth was not cakes or crafts (Clue 3), funny fotos or penny toss (Clue 4) so it was books. Warren made more money than Philip Standish (Clue 4) but not the most (Clue 1) so he made 65 dollars. His last name is not Burger (Clue 3), Glover or Latham (Clue 5) so he is Warren Brewster. The crafts booth was not operated by Burger (Clue 3), Glover or Latham (Clue 5) so this was the booth where Warren Brewster made 65 dollars. The girl who made 80 dollars (Clue 1) is Miss Glover (Clue 5) and her first name is not Beverly (Clue 1) or Lucy (Clue 2) so it is Julie Glover, and she didn't operate the funny fotos booth (Clue 1) or the penny toss booth (Clue 2) so it was the cake booth. Lucy made 40 dollars and the penny toss made 35 dollars (Clue 5) operated by the remaining kid, Beverly, whose last name must be Burger (Clue 3), which leaves Latham to be Lucy's last name and she operated the funny fotos booth making 40 dollars.

In Summary:

80 dollars — Cakes — Julie — Glover
65 dollars — Crafts — Warren — Brewster
50 dollars — Books — Philip — Standish
40 dollars — Funny fotos — Lucy — Latham
25 dollars — Penny toss — Beverly — Burger

48. BIRD HOUSES

Mr. Crane and Mr. Hawk are the two men (Clues 2 & 4). Martin is not Mr. Crane (Clue 2) so it is Martin Hawk and Jay Crane. The street on which Martin Hawk lives is not Birdsall or Fowler (Clue 2), Downs (Clue 3), or Poltrecci (Clue 4) so he lives on Winger Street. Jay Crane does not live on Birdsall or Fowler (Clue 2) or Downs (Clue 3) so he lives on Poltrecci Avenue. The three women do not own either the myna bird or the parakeet (Clue 3) so the men do, and since Martin Hawk lives on Winger Street he owns the parakeet (Clue 1) and Jay Crane owns the myna bird. Ms. Heron owns the parrot (Clue 1) and her name is not Polly so Ms. Raven does (Clue 4) and Ms. Finch owns the cockatoo. Since Ms. Raven's canary does not live on Fowler Avenue (Clue 5) she must be Polly who lives on Downs Street. Ms. Finch, the cockatoo owner, must be Robin who does not live on Birdsall Street (Clue 4) so she lives on Fowler Avenue and Birdsall Street is where Mavis Heron and her parrot live.

In Summary:

Canary — Downs Street — Polly — Raven
Cockatoo — Fowler Avenue — Robin — Finch
Myna bird — Poltrecci Avenue — Jay — Crane
Parakeet — Winger Street — Martin — Hawk
Parrot — Birdsall Street — Mavis — Heron